The bell rang close and loud, sending bolts of pain through Ange's head, not headache but agony of listening, of not understanding exactly what she was being told. She went on ahead of the others, hoping and thinking she was going towards the bell. And to where she would feel better and not be frightened.

'It's ringing somewhere,' she told Edward. 'In a place. We have to get to the place.'

Edward stared and stood. He was hearing the same bell, without knowing he should understand it, or that the bell was a sign to those hearing it.

Also by William Mayne

LOW TIDE
Winner of the Guardian Children's Fiction Award 1993

CUDDY

WILLIAM MAYNE

RED FOX

A Red Fox Book

Published by Random House Children's Books
20 Vauxhall Bridge Road, London SW1V 2SA

A division of Random House UK Ltd
London Melbourne Sydney Auckland
Johannesburg and agencies throughout the world

Text copyright © William Mayne 1994
Cover illustration by Ken Brown 1994

3 5 7 9 10 8 6 4 2

First published in Great Britain by Jonathan Cape 1994
Red Fox edition 1998

Printed and bound in Great Britain by
Cox & Wyman Ltd, Reading, Berkshire

Papers used by Random House UK Limited
are natural, recyclable products made from wood grown in
sustainable forests. The manufacturing processes conform to
the environmental regulations of the country of origin.

RANDOM HOUSE UK Limited Reg. No. 954009

ISBN 0 09 937121 9

*This is for
Clare*

I N the train to Durham, Ange switched the day off, weather
and all. 'We'll go somewhere else,' she told Beowulf, down
in the smelly cloth bag. That smell told her what island to switch
to. Beowulf might have been listening. You couldn't tell from the
outside; or sometimes from the inside.

Mum noticed that Ange had stopped being there. 'You'll have
to be sensible,' she said. 'If it was the dentist I'd understand, but
the man will only look in your ears for that ringing noise. Don't
sulk. And you don't need that old teddy.'

'Beowulf doesn't mind a bit of noise,' Ange said. '*I* don't.
We'll land at Cyprus, for a holiday.' They had done that once.
But now County Durham was going by outside, pouring wet.
Inside, stiff railway seats rattled. Ahead, Ange was to be cured
of something that was no problem; but you never know what
people will think.

At Durham the station taxi rank was wild with rain. Mum
could hardly see to the towers and spikes of the cathedral
beyond the city roofs, steaming gently like an ornamental flat-
iron.

In that cathedral someone was waking up. Ever since Ange
mentioned hearing a bell Beowulf had sensed danger with
reliable bear instincts. It'll be neither holiday nor picnic, he told
himself – quietly.

He had had a picnic when he was a wild cub in the forest,
talking bear language, more than a thousand years ago, long

1

before cathedrals. He had begun kind, and ended greedy; and the meal changed his life.

A young lady had been lost in the forest. She was praying and telling beads, and snow was falling.

Beowulf was on his way to bed for the winter, but he felt pity for the poor thing, and went to find honeycomb for her.

He took it straight to her, hardly tasting it himself; but when he got back he found her stretched out dead under a tree, snowflakes settling on her nose.

He had put the honey down and sniffed the lady's hand. It was quite frozen. After a time he began to eat her from the fingertips onwards, wrist, elbow, beads and stringy biceps. He was so hungry he swallowed bones, beads, sleeve and all.

A man with a bell chased him off, and his mum smacked him for keeping food to himself. It had been gruesome – *'Atelic,'* he recalled, in Anglo-Saxon. At last he had felt ashamed of his manners.

The man was a saint, called Cuddy, who spent that night healing the lady's arm where it hurt, and bringing the rest of her back to life. She was a nun called Elfrida, waking after a disgusting and devouring dream, to find it was true. Afterwards she sat in the snow with Cuddy, eating the honey. Then she went back to her nunnery, in a way.

Beowulf had belly-ache all night. In the morning Cuddy blessed him, and asked him not to eat nuns again. 'One day,' he said, 'I shall need you. You will hear me call. My sign will be clear.'

Later Beowulf understood his belly-ache. The bits of Elfrida he had eaten and partly digested had come to life too, and were now alive and kicking inside him, not at the nunnery at all. His bits of Elfrida were furious but, being a nun, went on aggravatingly forgiving him, using fancy names. No thanks, though, for curing a wicked set of chilblains on the hand he ate.

He never heard what happened at the nunnery.

Cuddy had not spoken for a very long time. But Beowulf was beginning to hear the promised signal. The person yawning and rubbing his eyes, in that cathedral over there, was sending a sleepy message.

'Cuddy needs me again,' he said, in the bag under Ange's feet in the taxi. 'He said he would.'

'*One* thousand, *three* hundred and *thirty-three* years,' said Elfrida, clicking beads. For all those years she had been arguing, praying, forgiving him. And deep inside Beowulf each winter the hot frenzy of the chilblains he no longer felt. 'He needs *me* too,' she announced.

'Didn't mention you,' said Beowulf. 'Ringing the bell in that building. Like that first time.'

'In a *forest*,' said Elfrida. '*Mid*night.'

'There you were, all gone to God,' said Beowulf. 'I knew supper when I saw it. Instinct.'

'A significant day,' said Elfrida. 'I *don't* hold it against *my* Bruin. Was it important to you too?'

'A calm day, snow on the ground,' said Beowulf, wincing at the name Bruin. 'Bears' weather.'

Ange had heard the signal all her life without understanding it. Now Mum thought it was a complaint and wanted the otologist to cancel it.

In the consulting room he offered to shake hands, but Ange put hers behind her. Mum smiled and said this is Anthea, and talked about hearing or not hearing and why didn't Ange do one of them? The otologist asked about headache and ear-ache, illness and allergy, where they lived, what Dad did.

'My husband teaches at the University,' said Mum.

The otologist knew Dad. 'Ah yes, Daniel, the palæographer, reading all those old parchments. We're related, in some way.'

He asked Ange to describe the sound.

'Clink clank,' she said. 'Like a sheep bell.'

'Let's have a look,' said the otologist, with warm fingers beside her ears, looking through the back of a round mirror on his head. When he let her head go he used a pinging machine for a boring game that Ange played truthfully.

'Where do you hear this noise, Anthea?' he asked at last, switching off pingers, and earside manner. 'Just at home?'

'Everywhere,' said Ange. 'I thought it was dandelion clocks. When I was little.'

'Yes,' said the otologist, wondering what disease to offer her, filling in time with a joke. 'What do you hear if you stick your fingers in your ears and block them up?'

'Nothing,' said Ange. 'I don't hear anything at all.'

'That question should have been asked a great deal earlier,' said the otologist crossly, his joke spoiled. 'It's not a medical matter, Mrs Bell, but environmental. You could presumably find what it is. There's nothing wrong with her hearing.'

'I could answer,' said Ange. 'If it rang.' But no one wasted diseases on her now she was perfect.

Outside, by the black railings and the brass plate, Mum said, 'He made me feel foolish, related or not. But that's the medical profession.'

Ange's turn was next. 'And you,' said Mum, 'never said a thing about blocking your ears.' She hiked off towards the grey cathedral. Ange followed, weather still spurting out of the sky, Beowulf thumping against her dawdling leg.

'I'm glad there's nothing wrong with you,' said Mum, briskly. 'But that's how it is. Stop trailing like a donkey.'

Ange felt her ears for fur. How did I know? Why does she

4

say donkey? *A creature of the Equine race*, she remembered from *An Infant's Bestiary*, at home, *With Upright Ears and Melancholy Face, His Shoulders crossed with Black on Gray, His Speech a sudden and discordant Bray.*

Mum walked round a puddle and tramped on. The donkey jumped into it with all four feet. Its white tights turned grey, but the donkey felt better. 'Where are we going, you know?' she asked.

Inside the cathedral Mum stopped marching. She cast a severe eye round the architecture and the huge columns holding it up, ready to find fault. But pillars and arches stood straight and steady, fit for any inspection. High bright windows poured rainbows from a stone-vaulted sky.

Distant singing hung in the air, like drops of new paint in a glass of clean water before the rest of the class turns it to mud.

'We'll have lunch here,' said Mum. 'That's what we need. We go through the cloisters for it, then we'll come in again and I'll show you something.'

A secret square of rainy lawn with covered stone walks round it made up the cloisters. Along one of the walks cathedral choirboys, in cassocks and surplices, hurried towards their stone vestry. Mum saw her cousin Julian among them, carrying a silver basin of smoke on cathedral business.

A group of priests went by, unlatching their cloaks, led by an official with a stick.

A big white cat sat in an archway, his tail round his feet, eyeing Ange enough to know her again.

A door clanked open, and a wet school came through, cuddling plastic bags of dinner, looking round for sweet-shops, or intricate souvenirs to last all the way home. Their nun checked she had enough children, counting Ange in and throwing her back. The school came out of its hoods.

One of the emerging heads was Ange's own little cousin Jude, with her reddish animal-coloured hair and sharp face. 'What's in that bag?' she asked. 'What are you here for? Have you been to the dentist? Did it hurt? Did you cry? I was sick when I went. I could come with you now.'

'We'll see you another day,' Mum said firmly, and trod through the school. 'I fully expect,' she added. Jude turned up for whole days when her own mother forgot about her.

'Don't lose your bag,' said Jude, holding the wrong end of it. Inside it Elfrida was wondering, should I make myself *known* to the nun, until Beowulf fell on the stone floor.

'Beowulf,' said Jude, kissing him. He was hugged by the rest of the school before Ange got him back.

As Ange and Mum left there was shrieking behind them. A mouse had come out from a crack in the flagged floor, and the school was chasing it along another walk, their legs scuttling like a herd of sheep.

'The man with the stick, their cloaks and clasps,' said Beowulf, as the clergymen went by. 'Those are to do with Cuddy. The place is full of saints.'

The white cat got up to see about the mouse round the corner, giving a hasty blessing with his mouth, quick as the word of God, as he passed.

'It is Saint William of Carileph,' said Elfrida, 'who once looked after Cuddy. We were *all* saints in those days, a good profession. But Cuthbert, our *Cuddy,* is the greatest.'

'Be quiet, Beowulf,' Ange said. If Mum heard him it would be Ange's imagination and Ange's fault.

The white cat came back with the mouse in his jaws. Ange felt teeth meet in her own neck.

6

'Good boy,' said Mum, putting out a hand. 'Let it go.' However, this was not a cat you could be familiar with, calling it that, or stroking it.

He swallowed the mouse in a gulp without chewing, raking his claws across the back of Mum's hand, and took himself up on the cloister roof. Mum washed away red water-colour under a dripping drainpipe.

'Not quite a sign,' said Beowulf, 'but history.'

Mum read out wheelbarrow and parchment pie from the restaurant blackboard. It turned out to be wild boar and pigeon. She chose liver, like the tongues of new shoes, polished edges gleaming under gravy. Ange had beefburger, different from home food.

'I never thought about blocking your ears,' Mum said, at the table. 'It'll be the army. We'll make them take it away if it bothers you.'

The army had Ranges on Ancren Moor beyond the fields at home. Guns would crackle like bowls of breakfast, or explosions rattle the house. Military sewing machines would stitch knots of smoke across the sky, and parachutists seed like gigantic dandelion-heads on the heather.

'It's a private sheep bell,' said Ange.

'We'll find Dad in the University Library,' said Mum. 'Tell him what happened.'

'Some of it,' said Ange.

'The good bits,' said Mum.

Before that they went to the tomb of the great saint, Cuthbert, a black stone behind the high altar. Jude's school had left drawings for him.

'There was once treasure here,' Mum said. 'He likes drawings better. There's a family story about Cuthbert here.

7

And about—' But she closed her mouth and shook her head. 'Well, no.'

'I have come to Cuddy,' said Beowulf.

Under the stone someone was sadly quiet at being disturbed by a small wild beast and being asleep in the wrong place as well.

'After he, you know, *died*,' said Elfrida, 'then he was like a *baby*. Sweet. All soft and tender. They *bathed* him. Once a tiresome pilgrim to the shrine sat him up and expected a miracle, but Cuddy was very dignified and said *nothing* though he was *very provoked*.'

'Didn't come alive?' Beowulf asked.

'For a *tourist*?' said Elfrida. 'No way. The monks made him leave before a *thunderbolt* fell.'

'I never tried baby,' said Beowulf, thinking back from what Elfrida had said and through his own long memory; chuckling, and teasing Elfrida.

Elfrida's beads went invisible bounce.

Ange was stamping on a wooden trapdoor that boomed under her feet, not attending to Mum.

'Stop that,' said Mum, continuing with her family story. 'Cuthbert was buried on Lindisfarne, but the Vikings raided and killed monks and stole everything. Cuthbert was rescued, and carried all over the north country, because nowhere was safe. He got here two hundred years later, and they built the cathedral for him a thousand years ago.'

Ange was working at the hard catches of the trapdoor.

'Ange, do come away,' said Mum, patiently. 'We're all descendants of the people who looked after him – me and you,

Julian in the choir, and so on – your cousins, mine, your father's, Ruth at the farm, Edward at the pub, Robin at Merrylaw.'

'Jude?' Ange asked, hoping Jude was not one.

'Jude too,' said Mum. 'I suppose. There were seven things to keep safe, belonging to Cuthbert. Of course they're all lost now, and just as well, because it can't be true. I believe the idea but not the seven things – a walking stick, a pinafore with safety pins, a hairbrush, a tankard, a dinner bag, all nonsense. But there's a ring, which sounds sensible, and there's . . . but that's a silly thought . . . all separated now. . . . What if they got found and came together . . .? Ange, *stop* it, please, he's down there.'

'The treasure,' Ange explained, opening the trapdoor. 'It's probably ours, isn't it?'

An odd left-over space crouched below, hiding itself in its own dusk, two walls straight, three curved, all stone, another person's private room.

A furry brown brightness, like a small animal, scurried across its floor. There was a twinkling like a coin running, and a sparkle of mild red light. Ange had a strong sense of knowing what the bright fur was – Jude's hair was the same colour – and of being down there as well as being up here.

The bell she had known all her life was ringing its loudest ever. Then the trapdoor was being slammed by a woman with a trug of garden stuff, here to arrange flowers, now acting like a small explosion, sudden and fierce.

'You should not be meddling,' she said severely, twigs flying about, heel knocking down the wood, Ange sitting hard on the floor, like being thrown there; but no one had touched her.

'No need to cry,' said Mum. 'You shouldn't—'

'Bit my tongue.' said Ange. 'And I'm paralysed.' She was frightened, too – the stalks of garden stuff had been hard as

9

steel, clattering like blackness in a nightmare, bringing a cold flash of terror to her daytime heart.

'The bell's ringing,' said the garden lady. 'Service starting early.' She gave Ange a metallic sip of water from a queer cup to soothe her tongue, then hurried away, scattering shiny beech leaves and white honesty.

Ange nursed wounds that hurt but did not bleed.

'Pushed me over when she wasn't near,' said Ange, trying to lick her tongue and look at it, rubbing her bottom, hoping memory was not real and would fade. 'I was just looking. Was she real?'

'Miss Norris,' Mum said. 'From Keld House beyond Ancren Moor. A lot of that family about.' She went back to what she was saying earlier. 'I told you six things. A bell was the seventh. The trapdoor squealed, but the rest was your imagination.'

'You heard it too,' said Ange. 'That time.'

'Me?' said Mum. But she would not say.

'All seven things have shown themselves,' said Beowulf. 'Staff, bell, cup, cloak, ring, clearly; some not clearly, wallet, hairbrush.' His mind was not wandering. He knew Mum's list but in different words. He always had.

'*Our* Cuddy is doing this,' said Elfrida. 'I, his sister in God, you, his *bear;* how can *we* help; what does he want? Is he *not* at peace?'

'Cuddy needs the seven things,' said Beowulf. 'He had them once and needs them again. Even people know what they are, but not where they are? And why does he want them now?'

'Outward and visible signs,' said Elfrida.

'Bears get inward and invisible signs,' said Beowulf. 'Most *atelic.*'

'That,' said Elfrida, 'depends on their *diet.*'

'If I knew what he wanted I could do it,' Beowulf said. But he did not know what that was, only that he had heard a signal about it.

'It was all written *down* somewhere,' said Elfrida. 'They can *all* read these days, so they have *only* to look. What *could* be simpler?'

In the library the white cat guarded a bright page in a showcase, with gazelles and a panther. 'An illuminated Anglo-Saxon Gospel,' said Mum, making Ange feel guilty at wanting it to be a comic.

Dad was in a work-room at the back of the building. Students were taking photographs of torn scraps of writing with a camera like a refrigerator hung from the ceiling.

'How did it go?' Dad asked. 'Your eyes are red.'

'I bit my tongue,' said Ange, and then remembered why she was in Durham. 'Nothing wrong with my ears. It's something actually in the environment.'

The student brought a developed negative. 'Very faint, Professor,' she said.

Dad held it to the light. 'Do all the fragments,' he said. The student reloaded the camera.

'People used parchment at least twice,' Dad said. 'This is a thousand years old, found on a hill farm. The farmer thought it was the manual for an old tractor, and used it to fix his gearbox.'

A joke, Ange decided. Dad went on. 'Words had been scraped off, but the farmer's thumb rubbed grime in and they began to show. It's a ninth century traveller's list of possessions, combs and scissors and aprons, and other odd things.'

'A dinner bag,' said Ange. 'A ring, and—'

'How could you possibly know?' said Dad, scorning Ange's thoughts, annoyed by interruption. 'There are illuminated

11

manuscripts you can examine in room 5. A student will start the projector for you.'

'But,' said Ange, remembering another list.

'Don't tease,' said Mum. 'Off you go.'

The manuscripts were two Tom and Jerry cartoons. 'Hand drawn, like the books in the library,' said the student. 'Sound is extra.'

'The lists are the same,' said Ange.

'Coincidence,' said the student, and left her.

The station at home was submerged in rain. In Ange's ears the bell began to ring, faint again but wanting a reply.

'All right?' asked Mum. 'Bottom, ears, tongue?'

'Something', said Ange, 'was under the trapdoor.'

'Don't put two and two together,' said Mum. 'Your father says it's all nonsense.'

They nodded wet heads to each other. Both nods were lies. Two and two did come together. The lists were the same; what happened at the tomb had a meaning, the day had a meaning. 'Should have gone to Cyprus,' said Ange.

'Tomorrow,' said Mum, meaning never.

'She knows,' said Beowulf. 'But what is it?'

'*I'm* saying prayers,' said Elfrida. 'For *you.*'

'That's all we want,' said Beowulf, alarmed in his part-Christian way.

Chapter Two

ANGE stood in the garden one morning and heard the bell clearly across Ancren Moor a field or two away. She felt that if she climbed the wall she would break through into another time, among the sheep, while still being herself. When the wind washed the bell out, the sound of Mum talking, and the smell of pie cooking, summoned her home.

I could have taken Beowulf and gone, she thought.

Jude Fitch was at the house, settling in. 'We'll have offices,' she was saying. 'And your dad's typewriter and borrow a pencil. I've brought my notebook.' She had a shabby thing that seemed to be made of sheets of cardboard. Ange and Mum felt sorry for her because she was so badly provided, but had to think herself best done by.

'Stay out of Daniel's room,' said Mum. 'He never knows where things are anyway. Play outside.'

'Offices are indoors,' Jude explained. 'I'll pop in and borrow a pencil. In offices they do.' She gazed longingly past Mum to the typewriter inside.

'Out,' said Mum, standing firm, knowing Jude.

Jude spent the morning trying to get into the room, and when Ange came back from helping Mum for a moment Jude had been in and made a fair exchange. She was still by the window, writing her own hooky characters on paper, not in the cardboardy book.

'That,' she said, without explaining what she meant, 'was getting full of Granny holes. It's very thick pages, too. I'm

13

writing about Mrs Beowulf. And toffee.'

Deep in Beowulf Elfrida blushed like chilblains at the thought of
Mrs Beowulf.

Something I ate, thought Beowulf. Toffee?

At dinner time Jude did not leave, but surveyed the table with
elf-like face. 'My Dad hasn't come back, and my Mum got up
late,' she said. 'We live like potters, Granny says. I'll just have
cheese, if you haven't plenty of pie.'

'Get your hands washed,' said Mum, giving in because this
was probably Jude's breakfast as well as dinner, and possibly her
supper too.

After the meal Jude tried to stay, offering to wash the dishes,
to do the gardening, to strip the wallpaper, or even do a large
and difficult jigsaw puzzle she had once seen – anything to be
adopted.

She sat on the draining-board and told Mum how she got her
set of parents. 'The doctor brought the wrong baby,' she said. 'I
belong everywhere else, not to them.'

Ange sat out on the doorstep with Beowulf and considered
leaving home, if Jude was going to live here and never get into
trouble like a daughter.

A pigeon walked by, strayed from a fancier's cree, tame at the
edges, used to a proper hand, eyes in its jerking head as roving
as Jude's. Ange thought of cuckoos pushing others out of nests.

She put her left hand on the shoulders of the pigeon and
scooped up its feet. It pecked her knuckles. It had a ring on its
left leg, plaited from tawny hair. Tucked under it was a coil of
dirty wood-shaving, which Ange pulled gently out and
straightened. It had upside down writing on it, but the other
way up the writing was still wrong, just scribbles.

Mum opened the door and scooted Jude out. The pigeon pushed at Ange's knee, opened its wings, and clattered away like a firework among the trees.

'Time to go, Jude,' said Mum. 'Edward is taking Ange to Keld House with papers for Miss Norris about the Show.'

'Edward is my friend,' said Jude. 'I'll go too.'

'Look after this,' said Ange, handing the scrap of papery wood to Mum. 'A pigeon brought it for me. Don't read it.'

'Yes,' said Mum, obediently, taking the message.

'Animals talk to me,' said Jude. 'I didn't know they could write.'

'I was going to give it another message to take back,' said Ange. 'But you scared it off.'

'My Dad got money for sending a pigeon back,' said Jude, sitting beside Ange. 'It told my Dad where. It was a parrot. Dad bought me a bike.'

To one of Ange's ears went the fables unfolding from Jude's tongue; and at the other the bell was being rung quietly and firmly.

'It was real gold,' said Jude.

'The bell?' said Ange, not hearing everything.

'The handlebar,' said Jude. 'Electric bells.'

Ange at that moment began to wonder about answering her own bell. A simple idea, like reaching up and pulling down the moon, or knowing without thinking that seven nines are sixty-four – The answer might not be right, but you must try. She spoke into silence when the bell stopped ringing.

'This is Ange Bell,' she said. 'Who's that?'

There was a response. Someone was grumbling gently, rather hopelessly asking for help to get himself home, if kindness remained in the world after all the recent troubles.

'It's Cuddy,' said Beowulf. 'I know the voice that spoilt my supper. He made me run away, then drew me back. He's talking again.'

'What does he *want*?' said Elfrida. 'Why is he awake?'

'Didn't say,' said Beowulf. 'If you stop talking and stuff we might hear.'

Ange cut the message off by putting her mind, like a telephone hand-set, back on its hook. She had no idea where it came from, or what it was. When she listened for it again, ashamed of being so abrupt, the caller was asleep. He snored.

'The reflectors were real cats' eyes,' said Jude, busy with fancies about the bicycle being more friendly than a pony. 'Boys came to look.'

Jude finds thoughts useful, Ange decided. I don't. This person should go home if he wants. That is not my business. I shouldn't listen.

Another bell rang, on a real bicycle. Edward Patten was wheeling at the gate, coming to see why he was here, having forgotten already on the way from the Swan Inn.

'No one explained,' he said, riding with no hands in a circle round Ange, 'but I'm glad to get away.' His mother's new husband had brought his fierce babies with hard skulls to the pub. 'That Smith lot at home is very smelly. Now they can crawl upstairs I can't get away of them.'

'I thought you could go across the tops to Keld House,' Mum was saying, 'by Ancren Dale. Just stay out of the army's bit.'

Edward was amiably ready to do what was arranged, taking things as they came. 'Where the three old bats live,' he said. He spoke as he liked, with his mother Mum's cousin, on another side from Jude.

'On the way back,' said Mum, 'drop Jude at her house.

16

Right, Jude?'

'Easy-peasy,' said Jude, ready to change it if she wanted, living hard from minute to minute.

Later she sulked because she was not allowed to carry the papers, even though she had arranged Beowulf on top of them looking out. Ange swung him in the cloth bag.

At the far side of Ancren Dale the moor came up to a fence. Beyond that the army rushed about noisily at times. A pole had a red flag, but no gunfire was happening.

Ancren Dale itself was a green place in the heather. A clear stream wound between green miniature hills, swung round a natural lawn, and meandered out of sight behind a crest of rock.

Jude, being ignored, went to sulk alone under a solitary thorn tree on the edge of the green.

'It's Paradise,' said Ange, ignoring her. 'Full of places I can just imagine.'

'You must look after me,' said Jude, trying to be lost among thorns. 'I am a seven-year-old girl and you brought me here.' She did not want to be helped. '*I* don't know Ancren Dale, *do* I?'

'That bell', said Edward, not listening to Jude, 'sets me wrong. I'm lost.'

The bell was ringing sweet, distinct and slow, swung by a gentle hand. 'Green and magic,' said Ange, calmed by it. Here it belonged; and if Edward heard it, it was real. She told him so.

'I don't get fancies,' said Edward.

'There's everything here,' said Ange, longing to step through to a better and blissful place.

'There's nothing here,' said Edward, looking round here and now. 'Except her. Well, there is someone,' he went on, in a curious baffled tone. 'Look, I can see him. I mean I can't.'

17

Not far off, beside the thorn tree, Jude walked oddly, as if she had someone with her. But she was alone. A sheep dog acted strangely too, running from side to side, dropping down, hanging its tongue out, looking towards the invisible walker, moving along a flock as imaginary as its shepherd.

'That's him there, with his sheep,' said Beowulf. 'Jude's got there first. What is happening? Why is he here?'

'Is he not *with* God?' said Elfrida. 'He should be at *peace*. Why is he awake and walking?'

Beowulf rolled out of the bag and under the stalks of heather. 'It's the forest again,' he said, looking vaguely round for another nun.

'Stop it,' said Elfrida. 'Just how many of us did you eat? What *else* haven't you told me?'

She's jealous, thought Beowulf.

'*Not* jealous,' said Elfrida. 'Worried.'

'I can't bear Jude around,' said Ange, not worried but jealous. 'Making things up. Spoiling it all.'

'How does she make it real?' said Edward, gazing at Jude, his mouth firm with disgust.

Jude waved. Then she took her companion's hand to hold his attention, talking and listening to him, walking backwards in front of him, clutching his arm and laying her head on it. Jude behaved like this to men. Yet no other person was present.

Jude on her own was a spoiler, but Jude acting strangely was far beyond tiresome. Ange's back crawled with dread. 'I'll just go home,' she said, wanting Beowulf, not finding him in the bag.

'She's acting, but she's not that good at it,' said Edward, standing still, not ready to leave, yet not sure about going towards Jude. 'The dog's better.' He gave Ange a nervous grin.

18

Jude tripped along, pulling that hand, her head flung back, replying to words only she could hear.

The dog looked towards the speaker for orders.

Jude rubbed her cheek on his hand, as she would with someone really there. 'Idiot,' she said to him. She smiled at Ange, happy with her friend, needing no one else.

Above the moor a curlew swung its twanging song, strange and far.

'Look,' said Edward again. 'Something.'

Between the dog and Jude a swirl formed over the ground, like air stirred dark by an aeroplane wing. In it a flock of sheep appeared, not squat and full of fleece, but wild and rangy, hairy like goats.

'We just couldn't see them before,' said Edward.

'Didn't notice,' said Ange. 'That's all.'

Her back was prickly. Nothing was explained.

Jude still talked to an unseen companion. 'I can't understand him,' she said. 'He can't understand me. No one does, because I'm like that, but he doesn't know English, and he lives here.'

'Who?' asked Edward.

Jude swung on an invisible arm, letting it take her weight. To Ange she said, 'Before you came we were having talk. And laughter. You could just go home.'

'Well, we will,' said Edward, looking at the sheep again, taking an uneasy step away from Jude. 'This is all wrong.'

'We'll come another time,' said Ange, angry with Jude for acting reality out of nothing.

'It's called New—' Jude struggled with a word, looking up to the invisible face to see it spoken, as well as hear it. 'I can't quite say it. New Oxen Wing. Daft, that's what. We're all going to his hut.'

Ange walked off, taking no notice. She sat under the thorn

tree, cross and frightened. You don't go to people's huts; but no one could stop Jude.

Jude was holding no one's hand now. She had her own on her hips and her chin in the air.

'Being told off,' said Edward. 'Making out she doesn't care.'

Jude was arguing loudly, but not winning. She stood her ground by the stream for a time, then dropped her hands to her side, clenched her fists, strode away, looked back after five paces, after twenty, and then not again.

'Going home,' said Edward, as Ange plucked a blade of grass and tore it to pieces. 'Gone.'

Ange tore another stem of grass to powder. 'Is it my fault?' she asked. 'We didn't play.'

'She does it on her own,' said Edward. 'Take no notice. I don't. She's always getting in our house, so I know.'

'I'll call it what I want,' said Ange. 'Not Oxen stuff.'

'Right,' said Edward, bored by that. The dog was no longer about, and the sheep were spreading out, some eating grass, others settling down to chew the cud. Their imaginary shepherd had gone too.

The memory of Jude stayed on the landscape.

The dog ran up to them, grinning, nudging Edward's elbow to show it wanted something to eat, prancing with its front legs, swinging its tail. It licked Ange's hand and settled behind her, a perfect cushion for her head. At her feet the stream turned its waters over and over. She felt comfortable again. High above a lark simmered and bubbled. Ancren Dale was itself again.

The dog got up, wagging its tail, and ate something it had been thrown. Ange's head hit the ground. She opened her eyes and sat up.

A shepherd was sitting against the tree, cutting flakes from dark cheese, and eating them with dark bread. His crook leaned against his shoulder.

The dog ate another scrap of his cheese. The shepherd looked at Ange in a friendly way, though without a smile. He spoke. Ange heard only a quiet rippling as if light feet danced on the bell.

'Perhaps he's Scotch,' said Edward, hearing the same things but in a different way. 'No wonder she didn't understand it. I don't.'

Ange was understanding, but not with her ears, replying to questions that must have been asked but which she had not heard. 'Ange is my name,' she said. 'I haven't seen it, or I'd remember.'

'You're making it up,' said Edward. 'Like Jude.'

'I know my own name,' Ange told him sharply. 'He likes it. I'm not hearing words but I know what he means. Bell,' she said to the shepherd. 'Yes, I understand. It'll be easy. We'll all do it.'

'Me?' said Edward. 'What?'

'He wants his bell,' said Ange. 'I know where it is.' Then the shepherd was correcting her. 'No, I don't know where it is. He knows where it is but he can't get it.'

Edward said, 'We'd best get on. I don't know what you're answering to.'

Jude was walking up slowly and wistfully to them again. 'I couldn't get home,' she said. 'I tried, but there wasn't any house, not even a road or a bridge. Just the church, but some bits of that weren't there. So I came back.'

It might be one of her tales of golden bicycles. Yet half a church sounded true, pathetic by accident and reality. Ange took her hand. Jude snorted, swallowed, and looked braver.

'I don't know what's what,' said Edward, looking at each person, and the dog, in turn. 'We should get off to Keld House and then home.'

21

The dog wagged its tail; the shepherd folded his cheese away in a wallet; Ange looked blankly back, having few ideas herself; Jude shook her head – with no village to go to there was no going home.

The shepherd spoke, ready to move on again.

'We'll come,' said Ange. 'We should go with him if we want to get back.'

'I could get home,' said Edward. But his voice was not certain, even if he was. Ange followed his eyes round, and found strange differences. Red willow trees grew by the stream, and they had not been there before. Harsher grass was underfoot, and the once clear waters of the stream were now opaque with peat.

The sunshine faded. Shadows had no edges, as if darkness seeped out of the ground. An unknown thing honked.

'Duck,' said Edward. They knew it was not and could not name it.

The dog stayed close to the shepherd's heels. The sheep fell into line behind it, and followed the shepherd upstream.

Ange looked towards home. The edge of the hill should have been heather, with moor swelling beyond. But trees grew there now.

'This is New Oxen Wing,' said Jude.

The shepherd corrected her. Ange heard 'Neorxenawang' with her ears; 'Paradise' came directly into her mind as the meaning.

They moved beside the stream between rounded hills of rough turf. After a turn or two they could not see behind or ahead. The sky tented the valley with grey.

'He's called Cuddy,' said Jude. 'I expect it's really Cuddly. He tells me quite a lot.'

'It probably means shut up,' said Edward.

'No,' said Ange. 'That's what they call him.'

Cuddy's name, like a piece of jigsaw, suddenly fitted two quite different colours and shapes together, making a different picture from the one everyday life expected. Ange began to remember, and almost to understand, stores of knowledge in drawers without labels, in rooms without doors, in houses without windows. She stood for the first time in this treasury, ready to ransack it.

But the world outside took over again, and the understanding faded. The dog stopped and stood with one forefoot raised, its head held stiff, the black coat on its back ruffled and bristled. It sang a threatening song in its throat.

The shepherd gave a caring look to his sheep, and another to Edward and the two girls. He said an unknown word full of meanings like 'Danger'. When he climbed the hill to face it they followed.

The top of the hill, instead of going on as moorland for miles, broke into a tumbled cliff with a beach beyond, and gulls calling.

'I didn't know seaside was so near,' said Jude. She did not think much of it. 'It's only sand, so we'd never go. We like a pub.'

'It's the army,' said Edward. 'The flag flying . . .'

The flag was not the red warning hoist of the army, but a black banner held by an armed man. Half ashore, half awash, a long black ship with a sail cracking in the breeze, stirred the beach. Its curved fore-end struggled live against the strand, with open mouth and wild eyes.

The distant honking came again. A man was blowing a horn and pointing with a spear. More men began to move.

'It's one of my dreams,' said Jude. 'Mum.' But yet again no Mum came for her, only men running from the ship, advancing behind a shield wall.

Chapter Three

'T HEY aren't looking at us,' said Edward. It was a prayer. He
hoped they weren't.

They ran back towards the valley to forget the black ships
landing and the men with flag and spear. It did not work. Ange
was wobbly, knees twitching and neck feeling sick.

'I'm scared,' said Edward. 'It hurts my skin all over.'

The dog urged the sheep towards the stream. The shepherd
strode after them, looking back when Jude shouted for him to
wait. He did not wait.

'You're leaving me because I'm the youngest,' said Jude. She
shouted to all of them to come back.

'Don't,' said Ange. 'They'll hear.'

The dog looked back, but Jude was not his concern. He went
on driving the sheep.

The sheep began to turn to mist. The shepherd lost his
outline and then his solidity, until he was no longer visible. The
dog found him, for all that, wagged his tail, and stepped out of
sight too, squeezing hard through a narrow place. The sides that
made it narrow were not visible, or touchable.

'It was all right until you came,' said Jude, trying to follow
and finding nothing but grass. 'Now I can't see him any more.
You are enough to make anyone moody.'

The moor edge turned spiky, with spear points and the
sudden loudspeaking of the horn, small, real, distinct, sharp.

The bell rang close and loud, sending bolts of pain through
Ange's head, not headache but agony of listening, of not

24

understanding exactly what she was being told. She went on ahead of the others, hoping and thinking she was going towards the bell. And to where she would feel better and not be frightened.

'It's ringing somewhere,' she told Edward. 'In a place. We have to get to the place.'

Edward stared and stood. He was hearing the same bell, without knowing he should understand it, or that the bell was a sign to those hearing it.

A shout came from the top of the bank, another from Edward, and a terrible scream from Jude. Ange did not look round. She ran along the narrow plat beside the stream.

Grass gave way to heather, brightly budding into flower. Running became more difficult. Cubes of fallen rock blocked the stream or lay in heaps across the way. The sides of the valley rose up more and more sharply on either side, higher and higher. They were no longer slopes but layers of rock in cliffs, making a canyon.

We'll get to an end, Ange knew. We'll find a modern road, and be safe. Jude was breathing and muttering behind her, made like wire, running like wire, her slim self all muscle.

From further back came a rattle of spears and the words of men. A shout of laughter sent a joke from mouth to mouth.

Ahead was the joke itself, not far off. The valley sides joined across the valley-gable, with a waterfall dropping down it, in a cliff too sheer to be climbed.

The escape led nowhere. There was nowhere to go.

Beside Ange ran a creature certainly not Edward. A gazelle leapt through the heather. They are chasing that poor thing, thought Ange, not me. If I stop they will go past. She was pleased with that idea, but did not want to stop running.

She was going so well, on the tips of her toes, her hands

helping her up the steepening ground, that to stop would be disappointing. Only in a dream do you go your best without trouble. My back is doing it all, Ange realized. That is the secret, to set your back running. She turned her head to see how the others were faring.

No Edward ran, no Jude loped. The gazelle was leaping in Edward's place. Where Jude had complained was now a sandy creature with dark muzzle and ears, bigger than a dog, liker to a cat, coming at a loping gallop. Its back dipped as its hind legs overtook the forelegs, and its tail swung high and low, high and low, as its back coiled in pursuit.

Ange knew it was a *Panther*, from *An Infant's Bestiary*, where it was *Pursuing its Prey over the Plain*, and which *will run at very great Speed like a Train, when in search of its Dinner, to avoid getting Thinner. And will kill not just Once, but Again and Again.*

This creature had chased Ange sometimes from sleep, coming into the room with her when she woke, and lurking near for several nights more. She had also seen it, with gazelles, in Dad's Library on the page of Bible that was not a comic.

She was in that drawing, a gazelle too. Hands did not help her, but forefeet. She ran in great bounds. The men with spears meant nothing. Only the lithe panther was real, and herded her along. Her skin crawled when she thought of claws striking, when she felt those teeth might dig sharp into her. Panther or men would eat her if they caught her.

I am more frightened of the panther, Ange knew. I am a gazelle. I am a drawing, and they do not know I am Ange. It does not know it is a drawing, and it will eat and kill me.

In daylight she was its prey, trying to outrun something coming as fast as a train.

If I woke, Ange thought, I would find Beowulf. But where is he?

On the edge of sight something neither man nor panther roamed the side of the valley, big, busy, observing. It was also worrying greatly about its duties and how to carry them out.

All sounds were now covered by the roar of water coming down the cliff. A claw flashed close to Ange; a black stick thrown by a man clattered on the rocky wall.

Ange's gazelle gathered its hind-quarters under and jumped upwards. She saw nowhere to alight, but the gazelle had chosen a narrow ledge smaller than a hand, and put four feet on it. The other gazelle ran up a wall to four separate toeholds, and looked ahead for more.

Another black stick thumped rock and snarled its way down the stream. The panther bounded across the waterfall, its eyes watching, its claws scraping. Ange leapt without looking, but the gazelle knew before it jumped that the end of the jump was possible. It stood at last on the top edge, looking round, the waterfall tumbling away below it, below her. And time stopped hustling by. It rested, switched back again to some sort of normality.

Below lay a charmed dale, steep and secret, filled with a soft haze of sunshine, empty of pursuers. Beyond the narrow upper glen sheep attended to broad pastures; far off hung the purple of distant hills, the smoke of a fire, wind carrying it stiffly away.

Ange saw her feet in trainers; her hands pushed hair back, her heart pounded from unimaginable escapes from being eaten, from being a gazelle for ever.

Edward lay calmly on his stomach chewing grass. 'I don't see where we came up,' he said. 'How can we get back?'

The panther rose up from the heather and sprang on to Ange's shoulders, pushing her to the ground. Jude's sharp claws dug in, her teeth snapped at Ange's face.

'I was a vermin,' said Jude. 'I chased you and Edward.' She

was so pleased at being powerful that she looked happy, laughing until her face crinkled above her nose.

Ange rolled away. She was surprised to find Beowulf lying face down. She touched him, but he was very heavy, and did not want to move. Out of breath, she thought, hoping he had come by himself, not been brought by Jude.

Edward was looking about. 'The red flag is flying,' he said. 'We can't cross the fence.'

The fence was strung round the head of the valley to stop the army falling into the waterfall. Its wire cranked round a small broken stone ruin with a doorway, a small window, and a fallen away corner.

'I hear a bell,' said Ange. 'Just close by.'

'Hearing things is bad,' said Jude. 'It might be the devil, my Mum says. I can hear a fly buzzing, that's all.'

The noise of the bell came and went with the wind. Ange shrugged her shoulders against the chill of moving air, and went with Jude to look at the old building.

'It's his hut,' said Jude. 'A specimen of a fossil of one. Who is he? I want to stop with him, Ange, I really do.'

The hut had a grass floor, a shattered stone roof, and a stone bench, or bink, along the back wall. The bell sounded as if it hung here, but it was not visible. Beyond the back wall was a sheep, or a machine, with a rough breath like snoring.

'I'll live here,' said Jude, 'until he comes back.' She went down on her knees. 'Don't look, I'm saying my prayers.' She closed her eyes, put her hands together, and murmured. 'Latin,' she said. 'I learn it at school.'

'You're playing,' said Ange. 'Don't. This is church.'

'I'm not doing it,' said Jude. '*Gloria tibi, Amen.* It's happening to me.' She began to lie face up on the bink, as monuments sleep in church, hands joined, eyes closed. 'Bed,' she said.

28

The bell stopped ringing. The snoring finished with a grunt. Someone was complaining in Ange's ear. She understood none of the words, but someone was not pleased.

'Who's getting cross?' asked Jude. 'Is it me?' She sat up, and then was on the floor, as if she had fallen off the bink. 'You pushed me,' she said, complaining in her turn.

'He was there already,' said Ange. 'That's what.' But who? she wondered. I got pushed like that; but what pushed Jude was friendly, even if he was cross.

'I fell out,' said Jude, climbing back on again and lying down. The shout that calls your name as you go to sleep, and wakes you, crossed the back of Ange's head.

As soon as Jude stretched her length, she rolled to the floor again. 'It's a game,' she said. 'You play it, Ange.'

'Hush,' said Ange. 'I'm listening.' A person peacefully in bed had found an animal in with him. Asleep was not quite the right word for his state. He had complained, and Jude had been thrown out.

'Smells of sheep,' said Edward, unaware of these things.

'It sounds of bells,' said Ange. Through her feet she heard the ground begin to tremble, a continuous movement and thudding. The noise changed to a giant scratching in the wall of the building.

'He's getting up,' Jude shouted, looking tensely at the bench across the back of the hut. 'I didn't do it.'

'It's falling,' said Edward. 'Come out.'

Before they could move, the back of the hut caved inwards, and a hefty blackish-greenish rod came thrusting through the stones, quivering as it smashed its way. Ange saw inside a long metal tube, shiny, and a swirl to its wall.

'It's only a gun,' she said, not alarmed for more than a second: she knew what it was, and that no one would point a

29

gun at her on purpose. Especially such a huge one.

The army brought them to the ranges all year round. Beowulf could have slid right down inside this one and been fired to the moon. But he was lying in the heather thinking in an ancient language. He had been away in some ancient time for a while, and was jet-lagged, not used to it.

'If they don't know we are here they might fire it,' said Edward. 'Soldiers do.'

'Not on people,' said Ange. The gun had explained itself, and had served its purpose for her. She crouched over the hole it had made, because in the hole was the thing she had been brought here for. She heard it move against tumbling stone, ready for her to take away. She knew its sound, its voice.

She plucked it out, stowing it under her cardigan, wrapping wool round it, hiding the lump with her arm. Someone was sure to think it was not hers, that she had no right to it.

Jude was talking to a worried soldier peering through the hole. He was wondering how to explain driving the gun through a wall and bending some working part. 'We're only Territorial Army,' he said. 'Part-time at weekends. We just borrow this stuff. I don't know what they'll say. Do you live here?'

A sergeant came to see what had happened. He fussed about the gun, but knew what to do, shaking his head at the accident. The gun went away, pulled by a truck. An officer came to look into the hut.

Ange thought she had met him before. He bent himself over and came through the hole. He knew her but had forgotten who she was.

'What are you doing here?' he asked, stepping right through the building and into the heather.

'It's ours,' said Jude, meaning hers.

'Well, ours,' said Ange, meaning anyone's but Jude's.

'We came up,' said Edward, pointing towards the narrow valley.

The officer looked down the cliff. 'I don't know how,' he said. He gave Ange another hard look. She now knew who he was. 'You want to go down again?'

'Yes,' said Ange. 'I've got what I need.'

'Have you?' said the officer. 'Anything you find here I'd better look at.' His voice was not quite angry, but was impatient and demanding. He had not spoken like this in Durham, examining ears.

What Ange carried grew heavy against her middle. It was bearing the weight of a rod of power, like the barrel of a gun, wanting to transfix her. The power was absorbed by it and did not touch her directly, but stray signals clamoured with dark voices, frightening her with tastes of nightmares – like the touch by the trapdoor in the cathedral.

She moved away, towards water tumbling over the edge of the cliff. In a trembling under her ribs, even her own voice ordered her to give the thing up to this soldier. But it would be better to go down the cliff than be forced to give it to this person.

Edward looked uneasy, and mumbled about giving the thing to whatever wanted it. 'You've got to,' he said, sure that something would happen to him if she did not give it up.

Jude saw what was happening to him, and sensed Ange's desperation. She was used to keeping herself together while battle and blows raged round her. She understood how to manage officials and teachers, and which person would do what she wanted. She knew that what Ange carried was Ange's own, and ought not to be given up and taken away.

She gave the officer a knowing look, picked up Beowulf, smiled her best, and walked across to the person most in charge, the sergeant. She took his hand and put him between the officer and Ange. The dread fell away from Ange, absorbed by a solid and friendly man. The sergeant asked to see what Ange had found.

She trusted him, and pulled it from the cardigan. It was a strange, large bell, not round but tall and boxy, with a squashed handle – like a sheep bell, but bigger. Its metal was brown and drab as leather, and it was empty inside, dumb, without a clapper. Yet of course it had rung. A decorative chain went round its skirt.

'Not army equipment,' said the sergeant. 'Sheep bell, or cow. Take it away home, pet, nothing to do with Army.'

'It's broken,' said Ange, making certain no one else could want it. 'It hasn't a tongue.'

'Well, he's an ear man,' said the sergeant, nodding his head backwards to the officer. 'Specialist in them. Doesn't have much to do with mouths, so we'll not bother him, eh?'

'It's all right,' said Edward. 'He can't have it now.'

'Don't trouble your head,' said the sergeant.

Jude was holding Ange's sleeve, which was a comfort for Ange. Beowulf was down in the grass, where Jude dropped him. She gazed at the sergeant's back. Her teeth were tapping on each other, with something not cold. 'That was him again, you know, the one I talked to. It was,' she said.

Beowulf waited where he lay. He could not do much about this officer at this time, but he was ready, if necessary, to move back in time. That soldier would always be there, and so would Ange and the bell, and Beowulf himself would then be of a certain size and nature. Elfrida was gabbling Christian stuff. Beowulf practised a growl and she dropped her litany.

32

The sergeant spoke to the officer. 'Best take them down on the nets,' he told him, really informing him what would happen. 'They'll not get down whole without, and the lads will enjoy a scramble.' He shook his head, because no one should arrive at places they could not leave. He gave orders.

Soldiers strung the end of the ravine with square rope netting. 'Right, one, two, three,' said the sergeant, and three strong Territorial Army men picked Edward, Ange, and Jude up, slung them over their shoulders, and carried them head-down through the spray to the foot of the fall.

Jude gave Beowulf to Ange, so that she could concentrate on her soldier. 'Up again,' she said at the bottom, clinging happily to him, shaking splashes of water from her panther-coloured hair.

'If you could *see* your *lungs*,' said Elfrida, still out of breath herself at the foot of the fall, 'you wouldn't get up to such *antics*.'

'I daresay they'll last me out,' said Beowulf.

'And *what* was that antic, anyway?' asked Elfrida. 'I felt most strange, like a girl again, like the old days. It was nearly *pleasant*.'

'I can't move about these days,' said Beowulf. 'Not now I'm a stuffed toy. But when the child went back to our times I went with her. Then I could shift for myself and keep an eye on things. I was a bear again. If it wasn't for that Jude I'd've had to be one in public.'

'I suppose I shall have to *put up* with being pleased from *time to time*,' said Elfrida. 'If I had a brush I could sweep out your *liver*. It's a ruin, Bruin.'

'They've got the first thing on the list,' said Beowulf. 'It's just beginning and there'll be more yet, so we're not out of the wood yet and it won't be a picnic.'

33

'WE have been waiting for these,' said the eldest Miss Norris, Miss E, smiling but not because she liked you. Behind her Keld House was biscuit-bright in the sunshine. Ange removed Beowulf and handed over the bag.

'Such a rough rackle-tackle journey,' said Jude.

'Yes,' said Miss S Norris, pulling a twig of heather from the handle. She never smiled.

Miss V Norris bustled up cheerfully and looked in the bag. She never spoke. She began to cry, in and out of smiles.

'Looking for sweets,' said Miss Norris, taking the bag away. 'Let her hold your animal.'

Miss V dropped a tear on Beowulf and then dropped him too. She really needed a sweet from the bag.

Miss S put an unsmiling arm round her and patted her. 'She can't understand,' she said.

'Handicapped,' said Jude to Ange. 'She's the nice one.'

One lady smiled and meant goodbye, one lady looked stern. One lady's nose ran.

'Thank you,' said Miss Norris, giving back the empty bag. Miss V waved a tissue gently.

Elfrida sulked. 'Oh Bruin, you let *anyone* cuddle you,' she said to Beowulf. 'Anyone *else*, that is.'

Beowulf ignored her when she called him Bruin.

'Keep it with your things outside,' Mum said when Ange

brought the bell home. 'You don't know where it's been. In a grave, perhaps. What is it?'

Dad said, 'Victorian fake medieval bronze tea-cosy,' proving his joke by putting the household one on his head, and becoming ridiculously unfunny.

Ange put the real one in the corner of the garden with her house-leeks, curly fossils, cat's eye out of the road, and white shiny pots left by electricity men.

She knew Dad was wrong: he had not been there. He wanted to be wrong. Mum smiled. They both want to be wrong, Ange thought. They know they are.

Silence held from the end of summer, into autumn.

'Yes, we'll watch, of course,' said Mum to the telephone, one afternoon weeks later. 'Don't forget to brush your hair, Daniel.'

'Watch what?' Ange asked. 'What has he done?'

'The stuff we saw that time,' said Mum. 'He's got something strange. He'll be on local news.'

'I hope they show the Tom and Jerry,' said Ange.

Later Dad was looking out from the screen, famous at home, at least. Few people, said television, saw what happened in the library, and how Daniel Bell recovered information from old sources. Ange again saw the camera like a refrigerator, and knew she was one of the few people who had seen.

'Professor Daniel Bell,' said television. 'Professor, how did this discovery come about?'

Professor Dad held up a piece of thick paper, but it wasn't. 'This is parchment,' he said. 'A sort of leather used for books. The original writing was erased, using pumice stone, and the parchment then roughly made into a book. It was here in the library, and no one knows how it got here. The sewing and binding seem to be about a hundred years old.

The parchment was older? television said.

'It could hardly be younger,' said Dad, with a smile for an idiot. 'The words are Anglo-Saxon, and the parchment more than a thousand years old.'

Startling, television thought one might say?

'Exciting,' said Dad. 'We took the book apart, then used image enhancement and found unexpected historical matter, which describes the hiding of a sacred object, to be recovered when the owner needs it.'

Television wanted to know what it was.

'I can't tell you,' said Dad. 'It's something to do with an island and a journey to it. Words are destroyed when a parchment becomes a palimpsest, and there has been vandalism since, words written with pencil; look, TOEFE, and MRS BEAR.'

'Palimpsest' bruised television's tongue, it said.

Professor Bell became lofty, and explained that a palimpsest was a re-used parchment, Greek for rubbed out; like a blackboard. Everybody knows!

White instead of black? asked television, shyly.

'Look!' said Professor Bell, waving it, 'yellowy, leathery.'

So this parchment was hidden in the library for a thousand years or more? television enquired. No one saw it before? Wasn't that extraordinary?

'We think it was in a box, with other things we were looking at,' said Dad, 'but not on the list of contents. We actually found it on my desk one day last week, just as if it had materialized.'

Television said that was wonderfully odd.

'You haven't seen his desk,' Mum told it.

Dad himself faded away. There was a quick glimpse of shadowy writing on a darkish skin, with one or two spidery words written in black over them, POOD and PASE. Then the

36

palimpsest of screen was written over with future weather.

Mum switched off the overcast.

Ange was quietly understanding that the sacred thing on the parchment was the bell she now possessed, and that its hiding place, the hut at the head of the valley, had once been neat with whitewash, the dwelling of more than a shepherd. Crumbling corners had come later, and knocking down by soldiers with the point of a gun this very year. The picture was crisp as a postcard.

Beowulf did not understand television. 'My eyes run at a different speed,' he told Elfrida.

'Bears are *ungainly* creatures,' she agreed. 'But I daresay they *have* a purpose in life.'

'The girl's thinking,' said Beowulf. 'The mother's done her bit. I haven't started mine.'

The bell murmured out in the garden, among fossils, a caller at the door of Ange's mind.

'If things weren't real,' she said, 'not actual, then I wouldn't know about them, would I?'

'You?' said Mum. 'You might; you've had your moments.'

The next day, among the bright china from electricity poles, the fossil shells and the house-leek, Ange said to herself, I know this bell is the sacred thing, as plain as food is the right thing when you are hungry. But what is it hungry for?

'Dad must agree,' she told it. But when he had decided he neither listened nor asked questions.

She tipped the bell up by its patterned hem. It brimmed with words, alive but slow. A man was giving advice, a woman responding, heeding and asking: a private conversation. Ange was uncomfortable about listening. Sometimes you know your manners when no one is there to tell you. She put the bell back to get on with its own affairs.

It was Saturday. Mum was making beds and tidying rooms. Dad was in his study out of the way of hoovers or questions about sacred objects. Beowulf was in Ange's bedroom window watching the gate.

As dinner was getting to the table a cyclist came by the kitchen window, a low-flying shadow. Mum said, 'It's Robin, Robin Crozier. From Merrylaw.'

When Ange was four and Robin was seven he had hit her with a stick, and she had not wanted to see him again, though they were first cousins. He had thrust the stick into the ground beside the gate and it had taken root on its own. Now it was an ash tree taller than Mum.

'Hot and hurried and short-grained as usual,' said Mum. 'I expect.'

Robin was. He did not waste time with greetings or coming in. He wanted to see Dad, and when Mum got Dad to the door, 'Where is it?' Robin asked. 'What is it?' His face was red with cycling.

'I don't know,' said Dad. 'I don't. I said so.'

'You said you wouldn't say,' said Robin. '"I can't tell you," you said. But you *must* know. Why was it on the news if you don't? I taped it and looked at it all night. You didn't say, but you know.'

'Time for me to go in,' said Dad. 'Work to do.' He closed the door on Robin. 'Who does he think he is?' he asked.

'Oh dear,' said Mum. 'Such a big lad now. I hope there isn't trouble. But what's he on about?'

Ange knew what he was on about. Robin was going back to his bicycle, frustrated, and ashamed of his pushy manners. Ange had things to tell him. She could not let him leave. She went out after him, took his arm and led him carefully through the house-leeks, and pulled the bell from its place.

'This is it,' she said, holding it out. 'He refuses to know, that's the matter with him.'

'What is it?' he said, touching it with his fingertips. 'It looks like a brown paper bag made of metal.' He was big enough to pull ash trees out of the ground and start again, and still not calm.

'It's a bell,' said Ange. 'I got it up on the moor. I have heard it ringing all my life.'

Robin traced the loops and whorls of the plaited band round its skirt. The bell sang a little under his fingers. 'I heard it once, in a dream about running away,' he told her. 'When I saw Daniel last night the feeling started again. I knew he was talking about something that exists.'

'You can't tell him that,' said Ange. 'Victorian, he says, not a thousand years old. You can't tell him *anything*. But this is what he was talking about.'

'I thought I was going mad,' said Robin. 'But now it doesn't matter what he thinks. Typical.'

A single note from the bell, complete and full as a whole melody, died away. In the calm garden on a warm day, nothing in the world alarmed them.

Something tumbled out of the house. Beowulf came down on his head on the grass, fallen from the window. The garden gate clanked open. Jude ran through with dinner on her face and a spoon in her hand.

'Sorry I'm late,' she said, picking up Beowulf and shaking him. 'He should be on a leader, Ange. I didn't even finish my beans. My Mum's at work so I get dinner the days I'm babysitted. I set off when it began to change. It does. Somebody—'

Robin wondered what this raving creature was.

39

Mum was outside now, to ask Robin whether he could behave well enough to stay for a meal. Then she said, 'Why have you come, Jude?'

Jude was working Robin out. She scratched herself, ran the spoon through her hair, said, 'Oh, I thought it was a fork,' and grinned. She was here, and that was why she came, she explained.

'I see,' said Mum. 'Run home when we have our dinner.'

'I had to come,' said Jude, sucking the spoon noisily. She gave the bell a ding with it. The bell grunted, and irritably knocked it from her hand into the little ash tree by the gate.

Jude put her hand on the bell, tracing the band of loops round its rim. 'Sorry,' she said, to someone she knew. A man talked, privately, about his needs. All three heard him, not eavesdropping now, but being spoken to quietly.

'Going on his holidays,' said Jude. 'To the seaside, Whitley Bay or Morecambe, I bet. We went to Cornwall once, and . . .' She was silent. She had not heard words but meanings that did not quite fit what she felt. The voice had spoken of going on more than a holiday. 'I want to go with him,' she continued, falteringly.

The world lurched. There was little more than a hefty quiver, but instead of midday it was dusk; instead of garden, barley was growing green; in place of the house there were trees.

Ange found herself ringing the bell methodically in a twilight clearing in time. She held its tongue and said, 'No one is coming,' to an extra person, who replied, 'Then we shall say it for them.'

'Where are you going, then?' said Mum, breaking into that world, but not being the person Ange had spoken to; just as Ange had not been her own self.

They were back in the twitchy reality of the present day,

staring at each other, unable to explain anything, as if they had each had a separate dream. Ange thought hers the plainest and least.

Mum gave up a plan to send Jude away. 'We have to wash these,' she said, turning Jude's wrists up.

Jude leaned against her. 'Not very fanciful,' she said, looking at them. She sometimes knew. Mum set Beowulf by the telephone, just as it rang.

Ange put the bell from the Moor beside Beowulf and picked up the telephone. She found Mum's cousin Ruth, from the farm, at the other end. 'I can't tell these days who it'll be,' she said. 'Do you want Mum? Bye, then,' and put the phone down. 'She didn't want anything,' she told Mum. Mum said that was a good thing, there was enough going on.

'They *pray* into that black bone,' said Elfrida.

'He rang *this* at me,' said Beowulf, by the bell. 'I ran away. Then he rang it at you and you got up. You were both very cross and *atelic*."

'Only with *you*,' said Elfrida.

'It's baked on,' Mum said, giving up the battle against grime at Jude's cuff. She turned on Robin. 'Not a word,' she warned him.

'If it's a civil meal,' said Dad, wary of sitting down with a quarrelsome Robin, or any Jude.

After washing up they were going to Ancren Dale, Dad's way of forgiving Robin, Ange's of forgiving Mum, and Jude's of organizing for its own sake.

Jude dried her spoon and put it in her pocket. 'The shepherd won't be there,' she whispered to Ange. 'Not with all them about. We can't be vermins in public. But there'll be

41

something.'

'Nothing to stop you going home,' said Mum.

'You don't know,' said Jude.

Dad was not impressed by the tussocky grey grass of autumn, and a brown mist down towards the village. There was little here to see; even the army had gone home. Robin looked beyond the village to point out Merrylaw five miles away, rising rounded from the mist, with a cluster of trees on top. 'Ours,' he said.

Jude was shouting, 'Hello, we're here.'

'Don't spoil it,' said Mum. Dad shook his head in a wilderness he did not understand.

'He's a friend,' said Jude. 'There's too many of us.' She planned to be a panther again, or at least be taken notice of. 'Enemies chased us,' she said. 'It was real life, not a dream. Soldiers.'

Round a bend of the stream, enclosed by faded grass, the sky turned grey overhead. Ange was ringing the bell at dusk. They were on a rounded hill with trees at the top and bare sides below. A man was praying, clearly, loudly and cheerfully for a safe journey through perils to come. What they wanted here and now was food.

Smoke hung in the air. A wild thing howled in gathering darkness, waking hungry too.

'Vespers for some creatures,' the man called Cuddy was saying, listening to it. 'Matins for others.' He made fire, catching sparks on tinder, blowing them to flame. 'These trees are sacred to pagan gods, but one stem will fight for our God. We shall cut it after the battle tomorrow.'

Smoke hung in the air. Ange gathered wood.

'What you do with what you have is what matters,' said Cuddy. 'That picks us out from the heathens.'

'I could do with any food,' said Robin.

'Also, what we do with what we haven't got,' said Cuddy. 'Make a virtue of fasting: we have nothing to eat.' He was always like this, pulling you back.

Cuddy's voice echoed among the trees. 'The woodmare returning our thoughts,' he said. 'In the coming fight we shall win, and so will the losers. Whether we shall live I cannot say. I have been a soldier, so I know battles are without justice.'

Men called at the foot of the hill.

'We'll lose,' said Jude. 'Let's go home, eh?'

'Choose that,' said Cuddy. 'It will give you purpose, but not necessarily life.'

Ange woke when the light changed. Dawn showed figures on the slope of the hill coming on carefully, not knowing what to expect, but used to fighting and fairly sure there would be no problem.

'Pray for their victory,' said Cuddy. 'They are on the winning side, like us; but it is too simple for them: we are not fighting the same battle.'

A growl like a vast war cry came from the rest of the world, as if it had settled under the weight of the cloud. Rain began to fall heavy and straight, rapping on heads, bringing down leaves and twigs, deluging the fire, surging like sea between trees.

'It is a sign,' said Cuddy. He embraced the torrent with extended arms. It darkened his monk's habit, and gushed from his elbows.

Jude sheltered close to his hem, her sharp face tight with discomfort. He pushed her hands away.

'Alleluia,' he said, walking to the edge of the trees. 'Alleluia.'

Jude crawled after him, unable to stand in the battering rain.

He held his hands out in greeting. His alleluias went on and on, merging one with another in a long war cry. The challenge echoed from the trees, throbbed back from the clouds, and rolled down the wet hillside. Men half raised themselves to see what numerous enemy would leap from the trees.

Cuddy's weapon came very soon, on the tail of his ululation, with a noise too loud to be heard.

A thunderbolt, bright as an axe, hurtled in abrupt and angry flame out of the sky. The sun was torn apart and flung into the midst of the trees. Rain stopped falling. Every ear was numb, and blackness was in all eyes. An immense bruised silence grew, then a prickly murmur on the hilltop, settling and crushing.

The army below covered blinded eyes, and dazed ears. It howled, threw down its weapons, and ran.

Cuddy lowered his hands. 'God has shown them they need not fight,' he said calmly. 'Now we shall cut my walking-stick.' For him there had been no strange event. He had utterly relied on his prayer and it had worked.

The cloud melted to a blue sky, and a true, undamaged sun lifted over the horizon.

The hilltop was a tangle of burst limbs cast down and snapped by lightning. Energy boiled in wounded trunks, and bark exploded from white wood; separated limbs loudly split their lengths; bubbling sap forced its way out, filling the air with scented steam; roots thudded softly under the turf, breaking apart below ground. The thunderbolt, now buried in rock, was boiling the blood of the trees.

One by one standing trunks tipped over, lifting roots to the sky. The noise increased to a shout, and subsided to a whisper, with every tree toppled.

'One of their groves has been taken to God,' said Cuddy. 'I shall tell the country how it was overthrown, and show it the staff I took from here.'

He picked up the nearest branch. 'God provides,' he said,

and handed it to Robin. 'Your knife will trim the ends.' Robin sliced off rough ends, and gave the stick back.

Cuddy looked solemnly at Robin, and then at Ange. 'You are guardians of my bell and my staff,' he said. 'Do not forget in times to come.' To Jude he stretched out a hand. 'It is a different thing for you,' he said. 'You cannot see it yet.'

Jude held his hand. 'Is it goodbye?' she asked.

'Yes. God be with you,' said Cuddy. He took his hand away, and Jude held the space it had occupied.

Cuddy turned and walked down the hill.

None of them followed. Something pulled them another way, until the whole of what they saw spun away into nothing.

Chapter Five

A NGE, Robin, and Jude, stood beside the stream, all three wrenched back to a more subdued life.

Mum took Ange's arm. 'You've had a long day,' she said.

'You don't know,' said Jude. No one bothered to hear her. She went to talk to Daniel.

'Walk by yourself,' he said, when she pawed him.

'All right,' said Jude, angry at once. She ran off alone. They watched her jump the stream and disappear through a field gate.

'She can be that way out,' said Mum, 'like both parents. She'll be back. But not today.'

She was wrong. Jude was waiting at the house for them, ringing the bell and complaining at being disregarded. She had brought Edward. 'He's fed up of home too,' she said. 'Those Smith kids.'

'She said you wanted me,' Edward mumbled, seeing Jude was not wanted, and himself unexpected.

'Ange wants us,' said Jude.

'I don't know anything about that, Edward,' said Mum. 'But you can see Jude home for us.'

'Not just yet,' said Ange. What had happened was as private as a dream; but Jude might have had a more interesting time doing the same things.

'I've told him,' said Jude. 'About the bomb.'

'Is it true,?' asked Edward, his long face anxious and curious. 'Would you get killed?'

'It was lightning,' Ange said. 'But not here. You remember

46

when Jude chased us in Ancren Dale?'

'She didn't chase me,' said Edward, unhelpfully. 'We climbed up and the soldiers got us down.'

'We were animals,' said Ange.

'I was a tiger puppy,' said Jude.

Their stories varied a little. Robin heard about gazelles, Edward about Jude's bomb, Robin's tornado, and Ange's lightning.

'It's Cuddy's bell,' said Robin.

'I spoke to him first,' said Jude. 'He's mine.'

'He rang me up before you were born,' said Ange. 'Also, my Dad read all about it.'

'Mine's too busy,' said Jude, needing to know best and have the best family, even if she and her bruises longed to be away from it.

'But that hill is on our land,' said Robin. 'It's Merrylaw. Daniel has got to talk.'

'Don't tell him anything,' said Ange. 'He's made up his mind and that's it.'

'So I'm famous,' said Dad, when they stared across the tea table at him. 'Daniel Bell is not just the world's palimpsest. He has a meaning of his own.'

'Ignore it,' said Mum. 'It's academic humour. You don't laugh, just repeat it to clever friends.'

'I wasn't going to laugh,' said Robin. 'It isn't funny. It's important, like reality.'

'The transcripts refer to things we don't know about,' said Dad. 'I have my ideas, and so have others. I hope they are ready to change theirs.'

'I'll *know* what it says,' said Robin.

Dad opened a file of papers. 'You couldn't, unless you wrote it in the Anglo-Saxon Northumbrian dialect and haven't mentioned the fact before.'

'It's a hidden thing,' said Robin. 'You said.'

'It's about travelling among the heathen,' said Dad, 'danger – *bealosith*; an enemy – *andsaca*; and death. As well as something *byrgan*, buried.'

'And what else?' said Robin. 'A stick.'

'That's not a secret,' said Dad. 'But it wasn't on the television. It's the cutting of a staff, for a journey, and fire from heaven striking a clump of trees to impress the pagans.'

Jude was quietly eating, a strand of celery hanging from the corner of her mouth. She remembered. She nodded her head. 'Trees boil.'

'How do you know?' asked Dad. 'You don't.'

Jude sucked in celery, nodded her head, and knew.

'Is that as far as you've got?' asked Robin.

'We only found the book ten days ago,' said Dad. 'I'll bring the transcript home as we do it, but you mustn't publish it before I do.'

'We'll just tell you what actually happened,' said Ange.

'I give up,' said Dad; and, 'That is not a proper attitude,' said Professor Bell.

Ange was sitting on Beowulf. 'If we'd stayed,' he said, 'I'd have found honey in the forest.'

'They *haven't* got the stick yet,' said Elfrida. 'This is Cuddy's journey beginning. But *where* to?'

'Honey's got no flavour without bees in it,' said Beowulf. 'A bit of spice. I wish I had my teeth. This girl has some fat bits close by.'

Elfrida was *silent* with jealousy.

Ange remembered something that had happened. She could not tell which life it came from, or whether she hadn't just put a collage together from scraps within the same long life.

There was a cloudy valley, mountains in the distance, and lakes or sea. They had walked down a hillside in twilight, a long bank of mist scaly as a dragon, a green eye watchful.

'Farmers are settled folk,' said Cuddy, climbing a field wall. 'We are in a safe place.' He was puzzled by a wire fence along a lane side, supposing it was a trap, he said, fingering its barbs.

'I wonder,' he said, changing his mind about safety. 'Flight before prayer, perhaps. This is not Paradise, though the name is like it.'

Chanting came through the mist, an unknown tongue calling to prayer, loud as bells, noise without words, invocations and warnings booming.

'Only a great church, surely,' said Cuddy, 'has so fierce a priest.'

The wire fence began to sing. The ground was buzzing, then vibrating, then shaking. Out of its noise grew a pounding roar. Whatever the voice had called was coming, very fast indeed.

The air was rattling overhead, and there was small but continuous lightning, shrieking towards them. The voice calling in the mist was swallowed up in a greater noise. Beyond the wire fence, ten feet away, the dragon leapt along its path, light and speed and armour. Its sound rose to a high-pitched din, then dropped gruffly away.

The Glasgow Express, signalled and announced at Oxenholme, tore through the station, switching up the line to Euston. Its tail-light flickered, and was gone. Its sound tapered to nothing. Loudspeakers on the platforms fell silent. The green eye turned red.

Sheep grazing close by took no notice. Prayers died on the

air. No fence now barred their way; no iron rail crossed the grass.

'Truly,' said Cuddy, 'it is an illusion that sounded like a donkey, and must be harmless.'

'It doesn't look the same, but it is,' Robin said a week later, after tea at his house. He was going with Ange to Merrylaw, his own hill, among their own fields. 'That's where it happened.' Mum and Robin's mother were having sisterly talk indoors.

'I don't want it to happen again,' said Ange. She had the bell, wrapped in Mum's pullover, gagged by sleeves.

Robin held back a thorny gap in a hedge for Ange. She slipped on a branch and fell down into the grass. The bell jumped away, ting-tanged on stones, and lay empty at her feet.

Ange wondered how to breathe, why the grass was so long in the bottom of the hedge, and why the world had gone darker. She tucked the bell under her arm, and looked for Robin. He should have been beyond a hedge, but there was no hedge and Robin did not answer when she called. There was only a thorn tree growing by itself.

'I'll go home,' she told the bell. 'I know where we came in, at the gate down there.'

But she saw only half-wild fields; and above her the top of Merrylaw was smooth grass: no trees, either living and green or dead and black. This was the same place and yet another time.

She wanted something kindly to happen. Nothing did. The sun shifted into the sky. It was dawn.

'But I just had tea with Mum and Robin,' she reminded anyone who might be in charge. The tea settled cold inside her. The last thing she had eaten was far in the future.

She was not alone. People were carrying a box on shafts across the field. Robin must have gone for an ambulance to take her to hospital, and these were the stretcher-bearers. But they ignored her and went up to the hilltop.

One of them was Robin. She knew his walk. And surely Edward was present, tall and long, looking grown, but the same? Ange thought she was there too, but did not trust her eyes. The party reached the top of the hill, set down the long box carefully, and levelled it with stones.

In the thorn tree something mewed and spluttered with rage, struggling and protesting. The tree shook empty branches. The protest went on, more and more solid, until what made it came into sight.

A thrusting hand, not large, not clean, held a branch, its owner still out of sight but screeching when thorns scratched the wrist.

In an explosion of kicking a well-known voice swore. A familiar person appeared, pulling the hem of her skirt from the tangle, turning angrily round and stretching to the ground.

'You won't help, of course,' said Jude. 'No, sugar, you just stand there. I saw you. You won't listen. First you aren't even home, and now I find you, you don't care. My Mum says your side of the family hasn't much sense. You do it on purpose.'

She reached back into the tree and brought out Beowulf. 'Taking care of him,' she said. 'More than you do. What's that up there?'

At the top of the bleak hill the party of carriers stood in their places still, ready to take the box up and move.

'I don't know,' said Ange.

'Nor do I,' said Jude. 'All those burnt trees have gone. Is he here? That's all I came for.'

Ange thought that it was Robin who came to the box and lifted its lid. A shaft of warm brilliance filled the summit, an uncommon light flooding from the box, dimming the sun. He

51

reached in and brought out the stick of wood, and closed the lid.

Jude was hastening to see what went on.

'It might be private, you know,' said Ange.

'I've seen private things,' said Jude. 'I dare look at anything.'

Robin took the stick to the top of the empty hill and thrust it upright into the turf. He had done this to a stick once already, at some time yet to be, in a garden somewhere . . . Ange shook her head but could not pull the memory into the past – some of it was the future.

The bearers walked away with the box, singing, out of sight down the far side of the hill.

'Come on,' said Jude. 'We go with them.' But when she and Ange were at the top of the hill, the bearers with their burden had withdrawn, and their singing had faded into rustling grass and the murmur of distant trees and waters.

On top of this bald hill now stood one stick. It pulled itself upright as they watched, settling with a shake, as if a hand below had tugged it firmly into place.

It unfurled a leaf and thrust out a burrowing root. The trunk thickened and grew. Buds burst with distinct noise, bubble wrap popping in Dad's document shredder.

With a simmering noise the tree spread a hand of green leaves. Jude looked at her fingers carefully. But nothing was sprouting on them. Bark creaked and the trunk split into two smaller limbs that thrust upwards. Grass round it heaved round the roots. The tree grew like a fountain, all in one season, one short time.

When it slowed, stopped, locked solid and stood still, the dawn wind ruffled the leaves of a tall ash tree. The branches, spread and arched, were solid at a building, a wooden cathedral.

Ange and Jude ran together down the hill, until they found Robin walking beside them. He had seen what he came to see,

52

and was calmly on the way home. He looked once at Jude, but said nothing.

Down by the road, traffic drumming by again, and an aeroplane swooping across the sky told them of their own day. Jude was no longer with them.

'I had a day-dream,' said Robin. 'I planted a walking-stick. But it couldn't be Jude with you.'

'She's in it,' said Ange. 'I can't help it.'

'Yuk dream,' said Robin. 'If this is the stuff off Daniel's parchment, he can write her out of the script like in soap operas. Cut the character, and send it to Australia.'

'Mum says Jude doesn't know much about soap,' said Ange.

The sky was leaden overhead, Merrylaw crowned by mist. The man with the gun was crossing the stile. His huge dog was indistinct behind. It seemed painted on the ground below, or on the hedge.

'Afternoon, Crozier,' the man said.

'Good afternoon, Mr Norris,' said Robin.

'C'm on, Fen,' said Mr Norris, going on his way with a nod. The dog sniffed the air next to Ange. Her skin twitched at this evidence of a ghost. The dog growled low, following its master.

'He shoots over our land,' said Robin. The reports of the gun went further and further away. 'That was the stick from the battle. It didn't last till now just as a stick. But it grew into a tree, and scattered its keys outwards, and all its descendants made a ring round where it was, on Merrylaw. I had to look after it, and I do.'

The next action was simple. They went to the house and deliberately got a saw. Robin carried it.

While Mum looked round near the farm for her, Ange was with Robin on Merrylaw, choosing a straight shoot, sawing it

53

off, and trimming it to the proper length.

'I cut the right one,' he said, turning the stick for Ange to see and feel how he knew.

She compared the hard metal of the bell with the green workings of bark. Round the rim of the bell and the shank of the stick marched the same unmistakable raised loops and swoops of pattern.

Ange got herself lost on the way down, straying into woodland so steep that her feet ran away with her, unable to stretch the strides her legs made, and banging down late and wild. She lost her balance and toppled forwards, bound to fall.

An ash tree was ahead. She reached forward, steered herself to it, put out her arms, flung them round the friendly trunk, and stopped her progress.

She had expected to be scratched and scraped, and have her breath knocked from her. But she found the tree softer on the outside than it ought to be.

Tree trunks had moss growing on them, but they should not have fur deep enough to cover her wrists. She was standing on more fur. The base of the trunk stood like the front paw of a dog, with separate toes and short claws.

Lumpy pieces under her left hand were not burrs, but the warm black pads dogs have on their legs. She had a handful of hair.

The tree trunk smelt strongly and wildly of dog. I'll understand in a moment, Ange thought. It's then for it and now for me. It'll be all right.

The tree trunk walked, lifting her from the ground, swinging her until she was thrown off and landed on her back. She got up on her elbows, ready to scramble away. Fallen twigs pulled at the green pullover.

The dog that had the tree for a leg put down a huge head,

opened a red mouth, gripped her by the pullover and shook her. It dropped her, sniffed, and rolled her over twice with its nose. It licked her and looked with one great eye and then another.

Beyond the dog something even larger stood black against the sky. Ange supposed it was a tree; then saw it was a bigger dog; then knew it was neither of those things, and far less tame.

The black animal put a hand on the dog.

I can growl, Beowulf decided. In spite of my liver.

'*No* brutality,' said Elfrida. 'No *sport*.'

'Just killing it,' said Beowulf. 'My job.'

'Close your *eyes*,' said Elfrida. 'I *can't* bear to watch.'

'Why are you rolling about?' Robin was asking her. He and the man with the gun, complete with dog, were beside her.

'I fell over,' said Ange, wondering whether she had screamed. 'I frightened myself, that's all. I thought it was a tree but it was the leg of something.'

'Is it?' said Mr Norris. The grey dog grinned.

'I'll take her home,' said Robin.

Mr Norris turned, called the dog, and walked away, looking about for things to use a gun on.

'That was a wolf,' said Ange. She still grasped a tuft of long hair, tree-hair, wolf-hair.

'Oh, aye,' said Robin, not bothering with fancy. 'A dog. You do get things turned about.'

In the distance a gun spoke again.

'Have you been through a hedge in my pullover?' said Mum, in the car. 'To pull the stitching open? It's loose-knit, so tease it back into shape.'

'Perhaps a wolf did it,' said Ange, teasing the wool as she was

55

told, as well as teasing Mum.

Mum snarled with the gear lever. 'Just be sensible,' she said. 'Normal and not strange.'

The radio reported a man eaten by a bear in Spain, a storm in Sweden leaving fish on house-tops, and a cat up a tree in Aycliffe biting a fireman enough to send him to hospital.

'Well,' said Ange, 'just look at normality.'

Dad carried a small thing between thumb and finger.

'Anthea,' he said, 'did you put this in my room?'

'I don't think so,' said Ange. 'What is it?'

Dad held a sliver of wood, aged and brittle.

'I gave it to Mum once,' said Ange, remembering. 'You can throw it away. A pigeon brought it.'

'How do you mean?' said Dad. 'What pigeon?'

'Message on its leg,' said Ange. 'Ages ago.'

'But it's a message in Anglo-Saxon,' said Dad. 'Saying, "With God's good grace we go this day to the island which is Neorxenawang". Explain that.'

'It's like on postcards,' said Ange, baffled. 'Wish you were here, New York's on a wing.'

'Don't be tiresome,' said Mum. 'Anthea.'

'Anglo-Saxon for Paradise,' said Dad, not very patiently. 'They didn't send postcards made of oak. Just that it ties in with that manuscript, but we don't know where it came from, so it lacks historical value. You're imagining about that shaving, and I'll disregard it. I'd say it was that Fitch child, but she can't write Anglo-Saxon.'

'Not her,' said Ange. 'I found it on a pigeon.'

She went to bed rather suddenly. Dad had borne enough.

'Where could he *want* to go?' said Elfrida, at half past two, time

56

for the first service in nunneries. 'He doesn't need a *walking*-stick. The world comes to *him*, in his cathedral.'

Beowulf snored. Nothing ever happened at half past two in the morning, except atelic times when Ange was sick.

Chapter Six

A NGE was helping Ruth Obley prepare the village hall for the
Annual Show, and staying with her all day. They spread
white lining paper on the long trestle tables, and covered it with
Class and Entrants' numbers on cards. Ange dropped the cards,
said her big swear, 'Oh heng,' and sorted them again.

Ruth, calmly waiting, saw Jude at a table, and went to her.
She gave her a marshmallow mis-shape unfit to exhibit and sent
her out, without raising her voice or making Jude cross. Jude
went out smiling, but doubtful of the lump of marshmallow.

Ruth tore the end of the paper from that table. 'She drew on
it, and left dirty fingerprints,' she said, folded it, and put it in
the bin outside.

They went round from SCHOOLCHILDREN'S CLASS, 57,
Six Peppermint Creams, to FLORAL CLASS, 1, One Rose,
ending neatly on the opposite table.

'Done properly it's no problem,' said Ruth. 'We'll go home
for dinner and come back with my entries.'

Jude was routing in the bin outside for the end of the lining
paper. 'Only scribbles,' said Ruth, and sent her a quelling look
down the street, to stop her following. 'She can't really want it.'

The footpath to Ruth's farm led beside the stream from
Ancren Dale, under a crag at the moor edge.

'It's Chapel Stack,' said Ruth. 'My Granda was seeing to
sheep in the snow and heard a choir singing at midnight. He
didn't know the tunes.' It was eighteen months ago, she said,
just a fact.

The footpath led over a turfy hump-back bridge. Ruth hesitated. 'I don't know why we came this way,' she said. 'This bridge fell in. Granda must have mended it, so we can cross. It's a longer way, but it's only eleven o'clock.'

The church bell was halfway through telling the time.

They were half across, on the top of the hump, when the church bell was cut off sharply with a twang in its seventh note. Sounds drained away to an inaudible soft click, like the dream that wakes you for its own reasons.

Ange had felt such changes before. Ruth thought the bridge was falling down again, and apologized. The world seemed shifted to a slightly different place, but they went on. Ruth was puzzled by the track. 'I'm getting forgetful,' she said.

If that was all, thought Ange, it didn't matter. Ruth would still be in charge.

Ruth paused at a gateway. 'We shouldn't have got here,' she said. 'I've come quite the wrong way.'

Ange thought that Ruth was never wrong. 'Is it Merrylaw?' she asked. 'Or where?'

'Just our moor,' said Ruth. 'You can smell the honey beginning. But the bridge isn't on the way, so how did we land here?'

Ange looked through the gate at heather stretching ahead. 'It looks nice if you don't know that,' she said, beginning to worry, wishing a big person was there with them.

Ruth thought so too. 'Dad would set us right.'

'Or a shepherd,' said Ange, beginning to expect one in particular, feeling better and safer at once. 'If we could understand his words.'

'They can speak very broad,' said Ruth. 'But I can get back from here.' She opened the gate and led the way. After a time she stopped.

The path had changed under their feet to the softness of beach, with the sea rolling small waves on shore at an angle, sucking the strand.

Ruth's eyes were wide, but her mouth stayed shut.

'Don't be frightened,' said Ange. 'We've got back before.'

'Not from here,' said Ruth at last. 'This isn't our moor. This is a field we have on the coast. Twenty miles off. We bring lambs here.' She looked back at the way they had come. Their footprints started in the sand a short distance away. 'There'll be my Dad,' she said. 'We must have come in the wagon this morning with the lambs. I don't remember. I wish I did.'

At the edge of the sea a dark thing moved. Ange remembered soldiers and black ships, but Ruth said it was a seal. 'They come up here.'

The seal was skimming flat stones across the water, playing ducks and drakes. It waved, and came sliding and stumbling across the sand to them.

'It's us he means,' said Ruth, waving back shyly.

'It's a girl,' said Ange. 'Wearing a skirt.'

Whichever it was it waved back and came scrambling up a low cliff. A boy and not a seal stood in front of them.

'Can you walk on your hands?' said the boy. 'I do it best of all the lads, and the lasses don't try.' He was about five years old.

He dusted the sand from his feet and put on his sandals. They had been looped in the belt of his tunic. He tied the thongs round his ankles. 'Where are you off?' he asked.

'Where are we?' asked Ruth. 'I thought this was one of our fields. It is. It should be.'

'It belongs the monks,' said the boy. 'Not to a lass. I was off along the strand gathering beads.' He cast away some little stony things, finding them of no value now.

60

'We're lost,' said Ange. She knew less about the place than Ruth, so she was not so puzzled by facts. 'One moment we were walking along a path, and the next we were here. It happens.'

'This is a path,' said the boy. 'What ails that?'

'It's not the one we were following,' said Ruth.

'But you're here,' said the boy. 'So this is where you were going. Come with me. My auntie will put you on the road.'

They followed him. He was telling them things as they went along, running backwards most of the time so that he kept their attention. 'I go to school at the monks', I look after sheep. I can run fastest and cowp my creels.' He meant he could turn somersaults. 'When I grow up I shall be a soldier. They have to be strong. I think I shall be brave as well.'

He went sprawling over a large stone he had not expected, and landed on his back, hitting his head on another stone not far away.

Ruth sat him up. 'You should look,' she said.

He blinked and stared, and shook his head. He said nothing for a time, because his chin was beginning to wrinkle and his face ready to cry. But he managed not to. He rubbed his head, grinned faintly, and stood up.

'All right,' he said. His grin slipped away as he looked round him. 'Where have you taken me? This isn't my auntie's.'

'Sit still,' said Ruth, unexcitedly. 'Your memory will come back. You live here, and we don't. But I shall walk on until I get home.'

The stone the boy had tripped over was on dry land, the one his head hit was in gravel, a third in the mud of a water's edge, and a fourth in water.

'Our River Wear, and our stepping stones,' said Ruth. 'It's two meadows to our home field.'

The boy was sitting up now, rubbing his head. 'Home won't

be far,' he said. 'It will be a gey long time before I get where I want to be. A soldier never knows where he has to go first.'

Showing off, thought Ange. Little boys do.

'We'll go across,' said Ruth. 'Our way home is simple.'

Ange went first, striding and jumping. The stones were dry, flat, and large enough for her not to worry about falling into the water. After a time water was no longer round her. The stones stood on misty nothing, leading over emptiness towards more emptiness.

'Go on,' said the boy, on the next stone back. 'Look at our swans. They're my birds, swans.'

'I can't move,' said Ange. She could not look. She could not reach to the next stone. Water was a shallow peril, but limitless space was deep danger. 'The river's gone away,' she said.

'Let me go first,' said the boy. He jumped to her stone as if empty depth did not exist. 'Queer goings on,' he said. He put his hand down to feel below. 'There's nowt under it all.'

Ange heard voices between the stepping stones, where water should have sung its way.

Ruth waited to come to their stone. 'We have to go on,' she said. 'There's nowhere behind us now. It's gone away, rubbed out.'

The boy jumped to the next stone and held out a hand. Ange thought he was too little to help her and followed on her own.

'I've sat here fishing,' said Ruth, taking Ange's hand. 'I never caught anything then. This isn't just right.'

'Not my fault,' said Ange. 'I don't know any better.'

'We'll see our far barn when we get over,' said Ruth, firmly. But it was not so. The stepping stones became a flagged path through a wood, cracked and tilted by tree roots.

'If this is our wood we can get home from here,' said Ruth, never giving up thoughts that felt sensible, but having to be hopeful, not certain.

The boy ran ahead. He spoke to someone, and began climbing a tree. Jude stood at the foot of the tree, watching him.

'Why is she in our wood?' said Ruth, walking steadily forwards over the coggled flagstones.

'She's stolen Beowulf again,' said Ange.

Jude's little face was set to the pain of not getting her own way. 'You sent me out of the hall,' she said, 'and here I am. I know who he is, showing off, but tell me the way back.'

'We don't know that,' said Ange, taking Beowulf.

'It's our land, but arranged wrong,' said Ruth. 'I don't know the answers.'

Jude looked very cross. 'I don't want to be on your land,' she said. 'A daft place to keep it.'

She threw down the paper Ruth had torn from the table. Ruth picked it up and put it tidily in the basket. Ange dropped Beowulf in.

The boy slid down the tree. 'I cannot see the road to my auntie's house,' he said. 'Will you not take me home?'

'I think we are lost,' said Ruth. She felt it was her fault.

'Oh sugar,' said Jude, annoyed with that, then cheering up. 'But I can stay with you, Ange.'

The boy was now down from the tree. He looked at them all to have their attention, and did his somersault in the air. He landed clumsily, and sat down, spoiling the effect. 'Roads go everywhere,' he said, getting up, pretending he had not tried anything.

The path led to a wet field, where golden waterblobs grew in clumps, and rushes clustered. Yellow flags, timid blue flowers, and hanging heads of soldiers' buttons were embroidered on ripe grass. Ange thought it would usually be pretty, but today it was alien.

Beyond the wet place was the dry mound called the Howe. Jude and the boy began to roll down it, until they splashed into a dub of water and started shrieking.

'This is our field,' said Ruth. 'At last. We'll share marshmallows.'

Wet people sat down and swapped giggles and mis-shapes. 'Nice,' said Jude, examining a sucked lump, 'but sickening.'

Ange was looking at Jude's scribble, straightening it between her hands, making no sense of it.

A shout came from inside the Howe, and running fast came into hearing; and into feeling too: Jude shrieked. 'Kicked up the bum,' she said, kneeling, her eyes following a queer echo under the ground.

'Granda heard noises here too,' said Ruth. 'He didn't know what it was, because he can't believe in fairies. He hears stuff on his own. We don't.'

'Specially me,' said Jude.

'It's like writing on both sides,' said Ange, turning the paper over, wondering what creatures ran in the ground below, gazelles, panthers.

'That's drawings off the lampshades my Mum made to stop her going mad at home all day looking after me,' said Jude. 'It was only my Dad wanted me, until he found what I was like.'

'The letters are strange,' said Ruth. 'You made it up.'

'Even my Dad can't read them,' said Jude. 'I never finished drawing this one.' She got out a stump of pencil, put the paper on her knee, and wrote again.

'It's nonsense, that's all,' said Ruth.

'It's just like Dad's stuff,' said Ange. 'It was on television. My cousin Robin came to see him about it. The day you rang up and didn't want anything.'

'Robin is my cousin too,' said Ruth. 'I don't know why I

rang, because I didn't want anything. Jude's seen how to make that stuff up, that's all. She couldn't remember it.'

'I can, easy-peasy,' said Jude, tongue going in and out like a snake's as she drew. 'She never finished them. She must of got used to me.'

The boy walked on his hands. One trod on a thistle and he collapsed to the ground. 'I'll do it again,' he said.

'It's time you grew up,' said Jude, jutting out her chin and being angry. 'Have more sense. You won't be any good until you do.'

'I'm off for a soldier,' he said, looking underarm at her.

'One day you'll find out what you are,' said Jude, 'and wish you'd started sooner.'

The boy stood up and dusted down his tunic. 'I'll get back to my auntie's,' he said. 'But you're wrong.'

Jude did not look at him. She went on writing and drawing. The boy walked off without looking back, whistling a little sad tune.

'You don't know anything about him,' said Ruth.

'He's Cuddy,' said Jude. 'Sometimes he's a man, and sometimes he's a boy. He's forgotten what he does later.'

Ange saw that he was Cuddy, and would be a shepherd in the end, not a soldier. 'Last time you were holding his hand,' she said.

'Then he was a man,' said Jude. She handed the paper to Ange. 'I've finished; you read it.'

'You've got too many wrong letters,' said Ange.

The letters became words being said, gently, by someone else. They spoke in Ange's throat the words of the page in an unknown language. She felt them move in her gullet, but before she could speak there was a thump on the grass beside them, and Edward was lying on his back after a mid-air somersault,

65

clumsier than the child Cuddy. Closely following Edward came his bicycle, its wheels still spinning and its handlebars twisted to one side. It capered on the hill and lay down.

'Are you all right?' asked Ruth, kindly, not startled.

'I came over the handlebars,' said Edward. 'In our inn yard. Am I dead? My Mum will kill me.' He sat blinking, looking dizzily round, waiting to come to his senses. His long face stubbornly gave nothing away. The back wheel of the bicycle ticked round on its own.

'Ange is going for her dinner with Ruth,' said Jude, alarmed but determined not to show it. She firmly sat Beowulf on the top of the little hill, to be in charge of everything. No one else was.

Ange sat harder on the ground, Jude's paper in one hand, grass in the other. She was dizzy too, and the world becoming different.

Instead of sky above, and earth below, there was a mixture, though not a muddle. Everything was clear, but out of order. The ground curved round overhead in a twisted ring that went over and under itself, a plait made of many strands of countryside and water, arranged in wandering loops and stitches, every way up but each right for itself, the same places in a different universe, and the sky between.

There were rivers, and the shores of seas. There were houses with smoke rising downwards; there were people and villages; there were clouds above hills, ships sailing; there were animals in small fields, stacks of hay, a wheelbarrow, moorlands with heather burning, bees flying in a cloud, a shower of rain and a rainbow in it, stags in forests, mountains touched with snow.

A horseman rode overhead, upside down, walking upside down. His road was his proper way up, and he saw nothing unusual. He sang a small song, plain and quiet, tapping his two dogs gently with a stick, because they were looking up to Ange on the Howe, and howling. The horseman did not see them in his sky. They would be on their heads to him.

'It's a dream,' said Ruth, 'we can wake up if we want. I'm going to.'

'You never can,' said Ange. 'Unless it wants.'

Far away in the pattern they saw themselves, sitting on the grass as they sat now, moving as they moved, not looking towards themselves, but at something else the other way.

'They're looking at our backs,' said Ruth. 'They're us. That boy looks like Robin.'

But that is not me, thought Ange. My back is smaller.

That other group sat against a dark shadow that burned. It was themselves at this same Howe, but on that mound at that time a black ship sailed through flames, sinking in smoke, falling to cinder. The ends of many oars lay burnt off and separate; the stern post had fallen in the ashy wake like a wishbone.

Here a worm was hatching into a dragon. It rose and flew over the group, having them in its power. It stooped upon them like a bird of prey, with dark wings spread. It held fire in its teeth.

Another person was now coming to that place, holding a staff, looking up, full of his own light, glowing with a suffused halogen coolness. When the dragon turned its long neck towards him he reached the staff up through the fumes, and touched the winged beast on its muzzle.

There was a shock like lightning, a roll like thunder, and the dragon softened to dust, its smoke and flame withered to dirty steam, and filtered to the ground.

The scene was now no longer clear in the twisted landscapes. But on the paper where Jude had written words were coming alive too, translated out of the unknown tongue, being spoken

67

by Ange's mouth almost in her own language, though not always being understood by her.

'It's a clasp and a cloak being taken care of,' she said. 'I don't know what it means. It says "bratt", and "morse". Horse, I expect. He says if we get them he can go somewhere.' The meaning pulled apart like soft toffee, thinning to a hair, and snapping. 'We don't know what they are.'

'Granda says we've got a field called something like Bratt,' said Ruth. 'He's very old. We don't keep horses now, but he would remember.'

'Morse,' said Ange. It meant nothing. The bicycle wheel ticked to a standstill. The interwoven landscape faded, and its memory dimmed.

'They've bred donkeys down to skin and bone,' said Beowulf, adjusting to the idea of bicycles. 'I never saw anything so short of meat. Worse than a nun.'

'I know where I am,' said Elfrida. 'The universe goes round and round, up *and* down, in *and* out. It never ends. From here we saw it *all*. If we keep on walking we'll get back *here* again. Everywhere happens *at once* in one place.'

'Let's just hang about,' said Beowulf. 'Was that smart cub Cuddy?'

'He was a *show-off* boy,' said Elfrida. 'A little acrobat, always the wrong way up, displaying his little *bottom*, never mind.'

'But that spinster is very sensible,' said Beowulf. He approved of Ruth. She was matter-of-fact, like a bear.

Elfrida went on and *on* with her geography of a *flat* earth with *crystal* spheres surrounding it, *and* angels.

'I shouldn't be sitting here, there's forever to do,' said Ruth. 'It's Show Day and there's my entries.'

'One of our Smith twins,' said Edward, 'put a stick through the front wheel.' He straightened the neck of the bicycle. 'Their Dad's nice, it's just them. I should be helping at bar meals, waiting on.'

Everyday landscape was round them now, field and wall, wall and field, barns in their corners and hay being cut. A red bus grunted along a lane. The world was farmland they knew, under the ragged high cloud of late summer. They walked through its steady fields. Ruth said, 'I'm not sure until I get home.'

When she did her mother said, 'Sit down. We don't get so many visitors out here. Shift up, Granda. On the long bench, you bairns.' One or two extra made no different at that table.

'Many a hundred have sat there since it was built,' said Granda. 'It never sees faces, just backsides. Gan on, help yoursels first, say prayers after.' Ruth's mother looked sidelong at him and handed him cheese. He cut at it with an old hook knife from his pocket. They ate silently.

Later on Jude dropped her fourth pickled onion, was silently looked at by the family, and nearly blushed. 'Them make ye bowk,' said Granda.

Nothing happens here, thought Ange, looking round at the Obley family. They cook and eat and farm and have no quarrels. Ruth's mother has never stamped her into a cathedral or sent her to bed for cheeking Dad. She has never had to fight.

'Granda,' said Ruth, when eating had finished.

'Why, canny lass,' said Granda, licking his knife, snapping it shut, and pocketing it. 'What?'

'It's Anthea,' said Ruth. 'She has read something somewhere that has to do with us. Tell him, Ange.'

They never speak, thought Ange. He will think it is important. 'It's about a fastening for a cloak,' she said. 'Being looked after by the people who . . . Where's the piece of paper?'

Ruth got it from the basket. Jude had rubbished one side with drawings, and the written side had turned back to rubbish too and was not being read to her. Ange could only say what she remembered, flying and faint as dream.

'They got land,' she was able to say, 'for looking after the thing that fastened the cloak, or apron. Bratt,' she added. Jude gave her a look and licked her knife like a Granda.

'It means something,' said Ruth.

'There's just a gill and its stream between them,' said her Granda, knowing at once. 'There's East Bratt ya side, and West

70

Bratt t'other. A bratt is an apron or a cloak, either. They've come down from my fore-elders that long that they belong to us.' He looked at the paper Ange was holding and shook his head. 'That's nought, you!' he said. 'And your father a professor.'

'I write them,' said Jude. 'She reads them.'

'It's a play-toy,' said Granda, turning over the paper. He saw the drawing Jude drew in the Village Hall, before it ever happened, of the path going round and over in its pattern. He looked longer at that. 'You've been in the stable and seen it,' he said.

'No,' said Ruth. 'I was with them all morning.'

'This drawing's a horse-brass,' said Granda. 'I've not seen it since we gave ower horses thirty year gone. Worth a bob or two, real aald brasses and that, these days.' He took a block of tobacco out and cut shavings from it, with the same cheesy knife, to fill his pipe. A match brought out blue smoke and black smell. 'In a box with other aald stuff, I don't ken where, just, back of the stable, maybe. Have it and welcome, it's nowt but iron, all the gold worn off. It's called a morse, you used it to fasten your cloak in aald times. They gan together like cart and horse, do bratt and morse. But then, I've near forgotten.'

'We'd best move,' said Ruth's mother, 'to the Show. We'll see this lot home. We can't foster them all day. I'll take the Land Rover for the bike.'

'When you look you'll mind the Haylock,' said Granda. 'He better likes the place to hissel, does the Haylock, and thinks it's he's. He won't harm good canny childer, only sorry ones. If you can have these things, why, he'll let you. If not, you'll not argue.'

Jude bounced off her own gate when Ruth tried to put her through it, and came to the Show instead. Edward went home for more dinner.

At the end Ange had thirty pence prize money and two blue prize cards, Ruth had a handful of cards and a cup, and her mother a bigger one. Edward had come back, and the sun was cushioning itself on a high hilltop.

'I suppose you can,' Ruth's mother said, outside the Hall, busy with other people. 'In daylight. I thought you didn't have sudden fancies, Ruth.'

'It won't last,' said Ruth. 'I'll see them back to the road.'

'I don't want to go home anyway,' said Jude.

'What are you looking for, Ange?' said Mum. 'Why is it so urgent? Just come straight back after. I'll be in the Hall tidying up.'

'I'll bring her,' said Edward. He was looking into the sunset itself. 'Helicopter coming.' No one else was interested.

'Enjoy your ride,' said Mum. It was one of her jokes.

The machine flew low overhead as they came to the farm. Jude waved. Dust lifted from the road and stung Ange's eyes. A long stroke of shadow went across them, and the bird flew on.

'Funny shadow,' said Edward. 'Feathery.'

The helicopter circled the farm buildings. Ruth's brothers, her father, and Granda, came out on purpose to ignore its sighing blades.

'They're cross,' said Ruth. 'The helicopter is lost, that's all, and they'll want to telephone. An air balloon did it once.'

'It'll be gone,' said Jude. 'Hurry up.'

The helicopter was settling beyond the farm buildings, out of sight, the noise of its engine dimmed after a moment.

'It'll be television,' said Ange. 'You and your mother got silver cups. You'll be on the news. Famous.'

'The cups are back at the Hall,' said Ruth. 'I'll look for the horse brass if you want to look at the helicopter.'

Ange had a vision of the helicopter that was so strange that she stood still. The others stood with her, sharing what she might have seen.

To the left, and then to the right of the stable, and then at both ends together, they saw the tips of bird wings extend and then fold, as huge as if they had brought the helicopter. Great feathers stretched out tense, and folded back with a loud metallic rustle.

Ruth said, 'That is not a helicopter.' She looked round for a refuge, but already knew that they were alone with the stable, the helicopter behind it, in a wide field. The nearest shelter was the building itself. Its broad stable door, and the double doors in the archway of the cart-house, were closed.

'I don't believe it's a helicopter,' said Ruth. 'It's made of bones. And it's like a thing that isn't there at all but pretends to be. We'll get in at the loft door at the end, up the steps and down inside.' She was making the best of what they had to do. They ran, ready to turn away, hardly able to breathe. Jude clamped fingers of iron into Ange's arm. Not panthers' teeth.

'Quiet for the Haylock,' said Ruth. 'I saw him once. He was so big, I thought he was a horse.'

A tractor trotted down a field. In the byre the milking machine sighed. The evening was normal but for a fancy about feathers behind the stable.

Ruth led them up stone steps. At the top Jude looked round the corner of the building at the helicopter. She fell off into the familiar nettles below. 'Get me up,' she whispered, jumping up and down, stretching up her arms. 'I'm not frighted of the Haylock.'

Edward reached down for her, touched fingers, grabbed wrists, and pulled her up the rough stone. Ruth held him from behind. Jude got her feet on the top flag, pulling herself up, terrified.

Something heard noise round the corner and came stalking along to see. It stood swaying, looking at them, part long-legged black bird with hairy legs, head with eyes and beak, but the body and tail of a helicopter, with white paint and blue stripe. Dusk glittered in windows and eyes. It was alive. It was here for a purpose. It did not need to do anything dreadful. It was dreadful.

Edward pushed Ange and Jude through the door, came in after them, and slammed it shut. 'Hush,' said Ruth. 'He'll hear.'

The thing outside poised and peered. Its beak rapped on the door and raked along the bottom edge, tearing at grass that grew beside the stone sill. It went away and settled down. When they looked from an air slit in the wall it was a helicopter again, until it rustled blades, like feathers.

'Guarding its eggs,' said Jude.

Ruth sat on a bale of straw. 'I don't imagine things, so when I see them it's sudden. I've not had any practice. I felt faintly, but I'm all right.' She rubbed her face, and felt better.

They climbed down the loft ladder into the empty stable. In the cart-house beyond stood a tractor, by a bench with horse furniture on it, and more tack on hangers above. Everything was covered with the fragments of straw and puffy dust of buildings, cobweb smoothing all the corners. Something walked the loft floor overhead, heavy as a horse, and the cart-house ceiling creaked.

The setting sun shone in at the stable window, and through gaps by the door, etching the wormy ceiling. There was the smell of horses long gone, and the unwholesome meanness of tractors.

Ruth turned over black leather straps of thick horse-hide.

Brasses swung and clanked, dull with tarnish. A door opened in another building. Feet moved on a stone path outside, and voices ruffled the air gently. 'It'll be here,' she said.

'Right mucky,' said Jude, shifting blackness.

'In a box,' said Edward. 'Your Granda said.'

There was a box, but it was immovable, made of sullen lead. The lid clung to the sides. Edward made a glaring new scratch with a horse instrument trying to prise it up. Then the box drew a breath in, and the lid lifted.

There was unexpected brightness in the grimy stable. Clean and fresh inside the lead a piece of sewn cloth was folded. It was embroidered tightly with a looped pattern they knew, but now red, blue, green, and sparkling golden wire. On top lay two short lengths of chain, joined by a circular clasp like a big new coin. The clasp bore the pattern of the cloth, the world of earlier in the day.

These were the bratt and the morse, the bratt worn about the shoulders as a cloak, the morse to fasten it at the neck. They had been here for the centuries this land had been used, safe in their box, now remembered, now forgotten.

Light rose from the box, warm against their faces. This room with closed doors and no windows glowed with it.

'It feels new, hot, prickly, electric,' said Ruth. 'But it's old, and these small stitches are magic.' Interwoven creatures moved on the cloth, like part of it.

Four of them stood looking. And one more, huge, hairy as hay, smelly, rough; a great hand on the bench, breath husking in a vast body, a head glimpsed by the corners of eyes, the edges of all senses. This enormous thing knelt among them, and the hand lifted the immovable leaden box towards Ruth. She picked the clasp out of the box, and its chains hung from her fingers, chinking against one another.

And then there was nothing. The Haylock had gone. Ruth held the morse.

'Not so sorry,' said Jude, her teeth chattering with scared joy; and she hugged herself, full of unknown sensations. 'Am I canny childer?'

Inside the lead box there was movement, and change. The dance of embroidered objects slowed, and they crumbled away. The light and the cloth rotted, darkened, and settled into dust, and there was nothing there. It was dim and grey as the rest of the stable.

Outside people were approaching with some purpose. Some other things thought they were sorry childer and should be sorrier.

'It's not our lads,' said Ruth. 'There's others. What can we do?'

'Run past,' said Jude, knowing such things. 'They think you're doing nowt if you don't try to hide. Edward can chase us, but don't catch us. Just playing. But wait.' She was dabbling in the empty box.

'Jude,' said Ruth.

'You're leaving stuff,' said Jude. She waved a thin banner of golden brightness, all the metallic threads of the bratt, twisted and braided. She held the skein up, arms wide, bundled it into a ball and stowed it under her skimpy cardigan.

They flung the stable door open and ran innocent into the field outside. Something large padded beside them in the dusk.

Beyond the building claws scraped. The helicopter had wakened again. Terror nipped their nerves. Ange knew she was not brave or sensible.

Granda was showing two men towards the stable. One was in uniform. The other, startled by an extra monstrous shape before him, lost his outline and put four legs to the ground, lifting its muzzle, something older and wilder than dog.

That turned and loped after them. The pilot called it back. It bared teeth at the Haylock, then dropped its head and drooped its tail, mastered. Ange, looking back across her shoulder, saw it become man again. The Haylock lumbered into the stable.

In the direction of the village lights were burning. Behind the farm the motor of the helicopter banged into life, its rotors swishing. It lifted into the air, and light swept the ground.

'It'll find us,' said Ruth. Jude crowded up against Ange and Edward, finding more comfort in them than in Ruth, whimpering indignantly, afraid and striving for safety.

Her whimper went from suppressed yelps to purr.

Ange thought of panthers, teeth and iron fingers. But Jude was talking, and not chasing or clinging. The sound of the helicopter dwindled.

'That is pagan,' Cuddy said. 'Heathens move in their old ways, disguising their gods, who have no reality of their own, and that is one of them.'

'Good evening,' said Ruth, taking charge of her farm now that another visitor had appeared. But no farmhouse stood where she turned to its door; only, in the twilight, one or two miserable field walls, and a muddy path where garden had been. The lights of the village were out.

'It's all right,' said Edward. 'This is Cuddy.'

'I will see you home,' said Cuddy. 'The morse is in your hand,' he said to Ruth. 'You have kept it since it was left here, on the land you earned serving me, keeping me from the Northman.'

Ruth held it on her hand, links of chain hanging either side. Jude tried to tease out threads of gold, but the tangle was too great.

'That is the bratt, the cloak,' said Cuddy. 'I must go back to

77

the sea with it, to the birds, and seal-folk, to Neorxenawang. At present I am buried under a church, and it is a great weight on me.'

'Seaside,' said Jude, leaning on him. 'I knew.'

'An island where there is enough for one,' said Cuddy. 'I can begin to tell you, now you are collecting the signs of my being.'

'You will be dead,' said Ruth. 'If you are buried already.'

'So it will remain,' said Cuddy. 'But that part of me between body and soul wishes to be on the island, and always did. You are my family, when you have put together my pilgrimage, and the things I had in life are ready to go with me. I shall fulfil a thousand year desire to lie for ever on my own island.'

'You tell us and we'll do it,' said Edward. Ruth nodded.

'We'll see it,' said Ange. 'And get it.'

'Just hang about,' said Jude. 'My Dad will find everything.'

'But from the fury of the Northman, Lord deliver us,' said Cuddy. 'Pagans are with us already, first and last, and do not want you to find the things I need. You have three of them, and when you have them all, I shall be present, and free to move.'

Ange thought these things to herself, or heard them. She came out of that far night to her own front door, opening it and going in. Mum was taking off her coat, Dad in his room.

'There you are,' said Mum. 'Time enough. Are you all right?'

'I was quite safe,' said Ange thinking of the Northman and his wolf, in the dusk outside. 'Most of the time.'

'And Jude?' said Mum. 'Edward's mother telephoned to see where they were. Was she safe?'

'Her too,' said Ange, because it clearly was so, in spite of feathered helicopters.

'I've dropped my *beads*,' said Elfrida. 'Saint Cuthbert's beads. He sits on the island *forging* them on the anvil of the mainland.'

'I wish you had been a fish,' said Beowulf. 'Brought back to life half digested.'

'And where was Bruin, when that *disgusting* Haylock turned up?' asked Elfrida. 'Have you *anything* to say?'

Beowulf knew what he had been, and where. Ange threw him out of bed for being too hot, smelling of Haylock, and rattling. But that was Elfrida's beads, cruciform encrinates, technically holy by nature, perhaps gathered from the shore by Cuddy himself.

In Anglo-Saxon, a bead is a prayer.

Chapter Eight

I T was half term, so one day was as good as another. 'We'll talk,' Ruth had said, meaning Ange and Edward and Robin. But she had picked Jude up on her way, like brushing against burdock. Edward cycled to meet Robin coming from Merrylaw.

'I thought it was just Robin and Ruth,' Mum said when Jude, who had not been invited at all, had walked in. Mum had made a flan, because she had won a First with that weeks ago at the Show, better than Mrs Obley (Second) or Ruth (Third).

'It's turning into a conference,' said Ange, meaning that it had got out of hand.

Robin came with a long stick strapped to the crossbar, a rag as a flag behind his bicycle, for visibility. Jude wanted to hobbyhorse round the rooms with it, but Dad came out and muttered about peace in his own house, please, Anthea, and is that a rocket, Robin? He closed his door and went back to work. Too many people had come, even without Jude.

'We'll go into the garden,' Ange said, anxious not to have Dad ridiculing important things, and hoping he would think they were talking about building a bonfire.

'Yes,' Edward was saying. 'They are the same.' He had the bell in one hand, and Jude's drawing in the other. 'Copied.'

'From a lampshade,' said Jude, precisely.

'She didn't do this,' said Robin, bringing the staff into the argument. Jude could not have seen and copied what he had to show.

Ruth examined the markings on the stick. 'It grew like that,

that's all,' she said. She considered further. 'It's a big all, because things don't grow like that even once. But what he said makes sense of things. I heard him. If I hear something it's real.'

She laid the horse-brass with its chains on the garden table beside the bell, the drawing, and the staff. All four had the same whorls and loops, like the long recurving road in the sky.

'When are we going to see him?' said Jude. 'Off on his holiday.'

No one had anything to say. All the memories were private as dreams, unshareable, not admitted to by anyone.

There was a silence. In it Ange knew she was about to show off in front of Ruth, just as Mum was doing with the flan. She picked up the bell and turned it over. 'Hello,' she said into it. 'Are you there?'

No one answered. She had been sillier than a dream. Perhaps no one knew what she meant.

'Battery flat,' said Robin. 'These mobiles.'

'Let me,' said Jude, taking the bell, listening. 'Yes, we'll all come. We're getting our dinners first. Goodbye, thank you for calling.'

Ange burned with shame. Even her knees blushed. This was her nonsense being continued, and she could not correct Jude without being told so.

'We have to go up,' said Jude. 'To New Oxen. Paradise.' And in spite of coming from Jude, this was not nonsense. They could not get away from the truth of it.

'It's how you hear it,' said Ruth. 'It must be. We'll go. It is true, isn't it, Jude?'

Jude's messages were fanciful; but not this. 'You could cut me up,' she said. 'I'm going even if no one else does. He'll be there.'

81

Ange led them into Ancren Dale, with Robin carrying a healthy picnic in a basket.

On the Army Range engines of some sort were raving in the heather. A hedgehog grunted under the thorn tree. Nothing today pursued them up the stream, along the ravine towards the waterfall.

'We've been right to the end,' said Ange. 'To the top.'

'You can climb up but not down,' said Edward.

'We got carried by soldiers,' said Jude. 'That's best.'

Robin put the basket on a rock near the stream. The rock would be a picnic table later on.

They walked to the waterfall. Ange hoped, and not hoped, that Jude would somehow change again and change them all too. But Jude was trying to be the day's most important person by complaining all the time. She had a notion that if she had to be scolded Cuddy might appear. Cuddy, and everyone else, let her get on with it.

'Nothing is happening,' said Robin.

'Well Jude,' said Ruth, 'what else?'

'Yes, Jude,' said Edward. 'You made it up.'

'It was true,' said Jude. 'True, true, true.'

When they came back down the stream they had to bend low to avoid the branches of trees. Jude, strutting in front, picking on anything to start a grumble, let a leafy stem fly back towards Edward.

Edward caught it. 'But,' he said, holding it away from his face, 'there weren't any trees here when we came up.' Now there was tall woodland.

A falling autumn leaf touched Ange's wrist, hot as a spark until she knew what it was and handed it to the ground. All about them leaves dropped, hard with frost, crackling like a wide slow fire in reverse, giving cold, burning backwards.

No one spoke, and they walked on. The stream ran into a clearing, and dusky light came down to the ground.

'Our basket,' said Ruth, with uncanny calm.

The basket was on a boulder as they had left it. They were not the first to return to it. From one side came a lumbering, dark, shouldering, hairy shape, smelling its way. With broad head and tusky jaw it reached up and butted and bit the basket.

The canes of the basket snapped and sprang apart under the teeth, the plastic bags inside ripped and wrinkled like laughter. The wild boar chewed the soft sweet food, swallowed, knocked the broken basket to one side, raked the ground for crumbs, finished crossing the clearing and went on its way, seeing but disregarding them.

Ange had a sudden dreadful memory of something she had not done. Almost she had put Beowulf in the basket, and then decided not to. She pictured him in it, ravaged and torn, at the moment of knowing he was not.

At this moment too she became certain that Beowulf was not only a toy she had known from the beginning of her life but a person in his own right, in his own way, depending on her to make the world understand him; and that his own self had made her leave him at home.

The boar went out of earshot among the trees. 'Gissie, gissie,' said Edward, using a farm name for a pig, but not loud enough to call it back.

Ange looked at Jude, next to her, almost as if she had been that lumbering wild pig.

'No,' said Jude. 'Didn't you feel me getting smaller?' She was disconsolate and had been frightened. Then she smartened, stood up, looked pleased, and was ready for anything.

Cuddy was there, talking to the others. It seemed that he might have been there for some time, with Ange and Jude not attending. Jude went to establish ownership. Cuddy put a hand on her head, and she was content. She squatted down beside him without interrupting what he was saying.

'They have a god of war, not of peace,' Cuddy told them. 'They bring him out at need. They worship him, and that must be wrong.'

'Thank you for telling us all this,' said Ruth. 'These little ones have missed their tea. They should go home. We'd all like to.'

'So should I,' said Cuddy. 'But I need more things to help me on my way. Before my people came from Angle-land to make England, there were British people here. One of that race tended me, and he put the objects into a safety older than he knew. The British people had stories that made strange things real for them, and for us.'

He told them the things he wanted, and where they were. He did not tell them how to get the objects because he did not know. 'They are from the times of the oldest people,' he said. 'They were laid to rest with me because they were part of my life and my monastic vow.'

'But you haven't got much hair,' said Jude, in her outspoken way, laughing at him. 'You don't need a comb and a pair of scissors. You make the worst jokes.'

'It's not a joke or we wouldn't be here,' said Ruth. 'Somebody wants her tongue slit.'

'They are important,' said Cuddy. 'When I had made the British understand what I was saying I cut the hair from their heads, to mark them for God. You would think that it hurt them, for they made a greater fuss than when they were dipped in the icy river. Barbarians are soft by nature and can't get on. But as for getting tongues slit, it might happen, with that keeper of the comb and scissors.'

He told them what that keeper was.

They saw why the comb and scissors might be safe with that guardian.

'It took our basket,' said Robin. 'And ate our tea.'

'How can we catch a wild boar?' asked Ruth. 'I don't think these little ones should be involved.'

'There will be help,' said Cuddy. 'This is the time, and there is always help.'

'Helicopters,' said Ange, seeing the matter as it would be on television, a treasure hunt; herself climbing down ropes, running through wild country, stopping people on the street, reading clues sent by people over the radio, the seconds ticking away. She said no more, because the last helicopter had been of a strange kind indeed, from a channel or programme she did not want to tune to again.

Then Cuddy was not with them. They were alone among oak trees. The trees were very large and straight, as if they held up a building. Overhead the roof they made was solid, and put the ground in shadow. Wavering strands of honeysuckle thrust up towards light, with pale leaves and little hope, a pinched hand of flowers at the top.

The oaks were well apart, because only the mightiest still lived. Three trees away the boar spoke to itself as it dug among roots, crunching what it found, its eyes piggish and angry, its rounded jaw scraping and biting. Its tusks were jutty either side, yellow and large.

A crest of dark bristle ran from its eyes and along its back, erect, tangled, dirty. In it, on the nape of its solid neck, between its ears, the greened brass shears and a comb of slotted wood were embedded. If Ange had not known what they were she would not have perceived them.

'That's what we came for,' said Ruth. 'But even farm pigs can go for you, and they're tame. That one is wild, and there is nothing to keep it away, and no way of getting near it. We have to do both at the same time.'

'We'd need a rope,' said Robin.

'A trap,' said Edward. 'A great big gun.'

I can't touch it, thought Ange. This is not *the friendly farmyard Pig, With Appetite both Gross and Big, Who in his sty will Grunt and Rout And Wallow in the clay about, To give himself a muddy Wig.*

The boar stopped in mid-chew. It looked round from side to side. It turned to face them. It began to trot forward in a business-like way to show whose territory this was, running towards the sounds it had heard, looking for their cause, turning its head from side to side.

It smelt very piggy, Ange thought. If it smells us it will know we are human. We think we don't smell, but that's how Beowulf knows me. No, that's how I know him, but what he really smells of is me last time I held him. Once he smelt of sick for a whole week. I was too young to know he was real. That pig is not there, wake up!

Then Jude moved. Her feet had slipped under her as she stood, and she wriggled to regain her footing. 'Oh sugar,' she said. The boar saw her and knew it had to act. It charged with its head up, squealing, its jaws opening, the tusks standing out like knives. Its mouth still had food in it, and saliva frothing as it chewed. It was a dirty and dangerous beast, the size of an armchair, and coming straight for them.

Gazelle, thought Ange. Now it is time to be a gazelle. She thought Jude would force the change. But Jude was clinging to Ruth, trying to drag her to one side. Ruth was trying to move a different way, so no one shifted at all.

Then, and as if they grew out of the ground, out of the leaf mould and from among the straggly grasses, two dogs were alongside the boar, crowding it, snapping at its ears, nipping its back legs. In another moment two more dogs ran up in front and began an attack of noise.

They did not dare get against its face and jaws. They snapped at a distance to slow it and turn it off course.

It stopped running, and began to weave its head from side to side, not frightened by the dogs, but wanting to be rid of them. It was very quick in its movements, and exact. It was no plain farmyard pig, grunting slowly by a trough. This was a true and wild animal, defending itself.

The dogs' teeth could not take hold. The throat of the boar was too thick and the skin too tough. To get teeth to that great gorge meant coming against the tusks. Sudden lifting movements of the boar's head made the tusks into daggers to plunge into flesh, or swords to cut it. The dogs were merely a nuisance, had nothing to do with the pig world, and winning the fight was unimportant. The boar was out of patience and decided to turn away.

It walked off, disregarding the dogs. They followed it for a little way, barking bravely. The boar ignored them, and the dogs fought one another.

A man on a horse came through the trees. He shouted and whistled. The boar hurried away. The rider reached out with the butt of a spear and began thumping the dogs with it, as if he were pounding something into a paste.

The dogs abandoned their fight when they were hit. Two stayed by the horse, jumping up to greet the rider. Two came back towards Ruth, Jude, and Ange.

Jude patted one on the head.

It stood up tall and spoke. 'Give up,' said Edward. Jude smiled – perhaps she had forced the change after all.

The rider's dogs sat calmly under his horse, rolling their

eyes; and Edward and Robin were only boys again, after all. They rubbed their elbows, grinned at one another happy and quick, and turned to the horseman. Jude, like a cat that has got its own way, licked her lips, tasting her own smile. Ruth recognized the horse and the rider. She lifted her eyes to the tree tops, and Ange knew where the rider had been, where they had seen him.

'He brayed our elbows,' said Robin, excited by the fight.

'I'll bray them again if you don't keep in order,' said the rider. 'His lordship doesn't want it to turn and lair up. We drive on to him, so spread out, walk with care, and slowly on. We want all done today, and home to our own land.' He lifted his spear, ready to ride on. 'As for you,' he said, tipping the point of his spear towards Jude, 'any more, and your sort'll be in the pond.'

Jude looked down at the spear point, its sharpened edge glittering. It was an inch away from where the ribs joined at the middle of her chest, the fourth button and the third button hole of her cardigan. She wrinkled her face, to show that what the rider said made no difference to her.

'You heard,' said the rider, and took the spear away. He whistled to his dogs, spoke to the horse, and left.

Ruth breathed out. 'He could have killed you,' she said, and started fussing over Jude, undoing the wrong buttons and putting them right, like a mother in a supermarket smacking her child for being run over by someone else's trolley. 'We'll stay together,' she said. 'Whatever we're doing.'

'I said you could cut me up,' Jude said, thinly.

'We could go back,' said Ange. But further back there was only indistinct darkness, the forest only a sketch, with distance and shape not well indicated, not yet drawn.

Pale across the shadows ran a little herd of deer on a curving path. On seeing people they started aside into the unready backcloth on swift legs.

'I was a gazelle once,' Ange told Ruth.

'You were a goat,' said Jude. 'I know.'

'You know too much for a little girl your age,' said Ruth. She did not finish her sentence clearly. They all saw something else changing in the grounds behind them.

A patch of dark was being rubbed away, lighter and lighter, or spreading like a drop of white paint on dark wet paper, the edge fanning out. Something came through the woodland, obscured by straggly undergrowth. Ange wondered if she was seeing the woodmare, echo itself.

'Let it go by,' said Ruth, stepping behind a tree.

A wailing song slithered from note to note, with gaps while echoes died down. A figure became distinct and separate.

This was how Ange had seen him in the cathedral cloisters, in a white surplice, carrying a cup of smoke. 'It's Julian Westow,' she said, knowing him, thankful it was not a woodmare.

He came through the trees, not very happily. His little song to drown noises of the forest came in gasps and gaps, wails and hoots. The silver basin of sweet smoke hung from chains.

He was busy on an errand and could not stop. 'Got to get to the sanctuary,' he said, mostly to Robin. 'They've taken up the floor of the nave and left all sorts of stuff on it. The vestry has gone. The cloisters, O God.' His voice wobbled. He did not know where he was, he said.

'Nor do we,' said Ruth more motherly than her own mother. 'But it'll be all right.' Ange felt homesick for more than Beowulf. Jude stared very straight, not giving away any feelings.

'What's with the joss-sticks, Jule?' said Robin huskily.

'We're having a service with incense,' said Julian. 'I'm the thurifer. I'm going to the sanctuary.' He looked bleakly round, wanting to be back in real life. 'It's a bad trip. Does incense smoke do this to you?'

'We'll show you the way,' said Ruth. 'I think.'

'I can't wake up, so I'm here,' said Julian, accepting the surroundings. 'What are we doing?'

'We're driving a boar,' said Ruth. 'It's in front of us, and they said walk on, so that's what we're doing. It's carrying things Cuddy needs, and we must get them for him.'

With a warning shout the rider appeared again, waving them on. The two dogs flattened their heads forwards to sniff along the air at them. They found the boar's track and bayed. The rider thumped with his spear, and they walked with him again.

'It's happened to us before,' said Ruth.

'A lot of times,' said Jude. 'Most to me. I do it best. We have holy catholic smoke as well.'

'It's Judith Fitch,' Ruth explained. 'Another cousin. Something's happening to us all.'

'I've got to get back to my school dinner,' said Julian. 'And not get my surplice dirty.'

THE boar stood against a square building. The stonework was green with moss and damp. In its wall was an open archway.

'Keep it out of the castle,' shouted the horseman, 'or it's a day wasted. Get along by the wall and turn pig, turn pig.'

His dogs began to slink along on their bellies, watching, growling, smiling. From inside the building came a noise like several people running upstairs very fast all together. There was also a sticky clacking noise, like Jude eating toffee with her mouth open.

The boar moved its feet daintily, for all that furniture of body, on slim shanks and little hooves.

The thing in the building scuttled hugely again. Ange was touching the wall and felt it vibrate. Soft ground underfoot sucked and shuddered gently.

The boar walked along beside the wall, turned the corner, and had gone. To follow it they had to pass the doorway. There they each waited, knowing they had unexpectedly arrived at safety, and no more need be done.

'That's the school,' said Julian, because that was what he saw. 'About time.' He began to enter the archway of a tunnel as long and wide as a big garage; and such a passage was beside his school.

'Oh, there's our car,' said Robin. 'She's taken it right through.'

'Soldiers,' said Jude. 'Oh, look.' She saw something at the

end of the entry, and went towards it. 'Our caravan holiday,' she told the others, her voice lifting in delighted hope.

'Oh, it's simple,' said Ruth. 'There's the farm, and no helicopter. We just walk through.'

Edward laughed. 'I didn't think I'd miss the twins. Look at the little beggars. But what a scrow in our yard.'

For Ange the bell began to ring again in loud alarm.

'Stop,' she shouted, without knowing she would. What they each saw could not be all those things, and must indeed be none of them. Ange saw Mum, with Beowulf beside her, the same size and looking worried. Ange's mind was saying clearly, 'The poor thing is thinking again,' and wanting to go to him; but other senses showed her what Beowulf was seeing: a hollow roofless yard beyond, the bare stone surfaces, and a thing like a huge pale scorpion moving on the stone.

She struggled to the front, pulling Jude back, pushing her aside; and Jude was fighting her. 'You can see it's not there,' Ange went on shouting. 'It's something else. It's not what you think. It isn't, it isn't.' She fought them all after that, to stop them treading into that yard, where that thing ceaselessly paraded; that yard that was not school or home or holiday.

Jude was overpowering her, pushing past her. But the others were crushing Jude, and Jude's temper snapped. With a defiant look at Ruth she changed that part of her mind, and Edward and Robin were dogs again. They were to bite Ange.

The dogs saw clearly what was inside the building. Jude could not expect that. One of them bit her, and the other took Ruth's ankle; and then both understood the building too. Julian had to be hit hard on the back before the image of his school and its dinner went away.

A small thing ran about the walls, the size of a cat, but still like an ivory scorpion. In Cyprus Ange had seen a weaving-loom made from chicken's leg bones, moving and articulated with scarlet thread and black wire. What lived in the yard had the same effect, as if the chicken were alive still. It ranged the walls and the floor, its array of legs drumming and thundering hollow and horrible, shaking the castle, coming and going, a skeleton shuttle weaving a fabric of illusion.

Small though it was, and strong, it was too large in some dimension to come out through the arch or any window. It was imprisoned in its castle.

'When I had measles,' said Julian, 'I was delirious. My hands could feel all the weight of the world just where my fingers begin, and it was the nastiest thing I ever knew, until I saw this.'

The inhabitant of the yard opened moist jaws and chackered at them, hungrily.

'Move on,' shouted the horseman.

'I got bitten,' said Jude. 'Give me a ride.'

'Not you,' said the horseman. 'Drowning is for your sort.'

What was inside the hollow building filled Ange's head as it had filled the courtyard, unable to escape, and sounding, sounding.

'It's me inside myself,' she said to Ruth privately. 'What I am like.'

'It's all of us,' said Ruth, comfortably accepting changes in what she saw. 'My mother says we don't have good manners because we are perfect, but because we're wild. That's too wild to let out. Someone keeps it in.'

The wilderness paced and pounded, struggled and haunted, in Ange's mind. Then she laughed.

'What are you snuffling about?' asked Ruth, thinking she was being mocked.

'I was just thinking', said Ange, 'that Beowulf is like that inside too. My teddy.' Ruth did not understand that, because her teddies had long been switched off.

Behind them the building became less clear, merging into the shade of trees, falling out of drawing. Against its wall a large furry animal was eating another pink one on the ground. Not at all switched off.

They were shouted at from both sides to walk on. Ahead, trees were sharper than real.

At the end of a grove the boar stood at guard, head lowered, waiting and listening. It backed in a circle, unable to see or scent danger, but hearing noises all round, slight yet persistent.

It plunged through bushes, splashed through mire.

Ange heard noises behind them. Like those the boar heard, they made her uneasy at first.

On their right the horseman and his dogs now rode closer. Beyond him were men with sticks. Birds flew from their feet, things climbed trees, and a hissing creature spat.

'Wild cat,' said Jude, beginning to think again.

Ange took her arm. 'Don't you dare,' she said.

A distant horn sounded. A reply came, and another, and another yet. Under those notes were others of a different music, far and faint, further and fading, from whatever sings in forests.

'They've seen it,' said the horseman, listening to the horns. 'They're ready for it. We drive it to the spears. Wait, wait.'

It was a long wait, and they were not allowed to speak. The forest was as still as paint, except for a small wind scuffing the tree tops.

'If it gets killed,' said Robin.

'It would not be fair,' said Edward.

Jude sat and sulked. No one cared about her nipped ankle, and neither dog would confess to tasting her.

Ange heard the distant singing now and then. Many other small noises filled the silence. She thought she heard her own bell, far off.

'Cuddy,' said Jude, hearing it too. 'We must take the boar to him, not to their spears. We are not going to kill it.' She stood up.

The shaft of the spear came swinging over and caught her across the back, so that she fell down. She looked bitter, but happy too. She stayed on all fours and did not weep. 'Of course,' she said, shaking her head, unsurprised. Ange expected her to spit out broken ribs.

'Of course,' said Ruth, holding Jude to comfort her. Jude clung, and then let go, thinking of other things, used to sudden blows.

Jude was no longer there among them.

'She's gone away,' said Ruth. 'And the horseman, the dogs.'

The forest filled with a queer intensity. The air between the trees became more visible and radiant, a stage glowing from invisible footlights, hidden spotlights, already in action. Somewhere beyond the radiance Jude moved on her own errand.

The others were alone in the shadows, in a theatre of the forest where performance had begun with the curtain rising.

'We're them,' said Ange. 'We're the people doing the play. We have to go on. We have to go on walking.'

'We don't know any words,' said Robin.

'We'll just walk,' said Julian. 'I'll go first because I have my cassock and surplice on.'

'Jude,' said Ruth. 'Jude, come back, please.'

In one place there was music burning, a plain straight church song in firm voices. In another men were shouting in a different way, hounds were calling, and horns blasting in haphazard concert.

'The boar,' said Edward. 'It's got away of them.'

They walked forward together, down the central aisle of trees, on a smooth floor of gentle grass, a rayless sunshine filtering warm from a sky they could not see.

An array of tree trunks stretched mistily away on all sides, without dying completely into darkness. The forest was complete, the regular glades opening out into a vast orchard of oak.

Deer walked in it, creatures like sacks scratched themselves; or a pack like a carpet trotted silently, wolves in their wanderings.

Here Beowulf could be himself again, Ange knew; here he would have the wild things of the forests in his head and in his heart, and sit like a sack to scratch himself, as the bears in the forest were doing.

Ahead of them, calm as tapestry, the boar walked towards some decided destination, not caring that it was followed, snuffling the sort of welcoming grunt of a tame pig seeing the bucket of swill.

Light from the treetops came down blotched with colour, like the cathedral windows. Flat stone was underfoot. A rumbling reverberant echo hung round them, as if some great sound-wardrobe like the cathedral organ had moved in the enormous building, scraping the ground before settling.

The curved vaults closed overhead. There was a doorway, with more forest or cathedral beyond.

Beyond it stone took over, and the tree trunks were no longer of wood. No leaves hung overhead, and the place was enclosed by walls.

The boar hesitated at this entry, then rubbed its flank on the stone base of a pillar, and went through, questing but patient.

The next arches were of a lighter, richer stone, like biscuit. After that came pillars the colour of marzipan; then light began to seep from the surface of something like glass.

A wall went across, with carving growing on it, loops of stone creeper, darkness peeping through.

In front of this wall stood a man in long clothes with embroidered edges. Approaching him was the boar, going edgily, unsure of itself, but seeing nowhere else to be. Somewhere beyond this enclosure, this chancel in the woodland, the rumpus of a hunt was in full cry.

'What are they chasing?' said Ruth, looking round for Jude. She was of course not there. 'It's dangerous to wander off.'

The man had some sort of spear in his hand. He leaned on it, watched the boar, and waited.

Ange thought he must kill it after all. Perhaps the boar thought the same, because it looked round, turned to face her, and then faced the man again.

They were inside a sort of chapel. The walls were bone-yellow and not severely straight. On a table candles were burning, their flames glinting on a silver plate, a silver goblet, turning them gold.

'Gissie, gissie,' said Edward, half-heartedly, thinking of calling the boar away but not doing so.

'I don't want to see,' said Robin.

'This should be the sanctuary,' said Julian. 'But it isn't.'

'This is the sanctuary,' said the man. 'You have brought the boar to me. It has wandered the countries of the mind ever since I left them myself.'

'Then you won't be killing him?' said Ruth.

'We don't want you to,' said Ange. 'We had to chase it, because we were told to, but we don't want you to kill it.'

'Who is it?' said Julian forcing himself to be in the cathedral but failing. 'The verger?'

'Cuddy,' said Ange. 'He's our friend. We don't have any

problems with him.'

Cuddy was talking to the boar, not using words but sounds to coax and calm, to cajole and encourage. The boar responded with suspicious grunts and quick looks to see exactly where Cuddy was, in case an attack had to be made. It came forward, and little by little extended its head towards Cuddy's outstretched hand.

Each candle gave a sparkly light, like a handful of broken Christmas bauble, rubbed with colour all over. Julian went forward, swinging his cup of smoke, making the incense fume on its coals. The boar lifted its muzzle to that scent, grunting, and snuffing up the soft reek.

Cuddy supported himself with his staff. It was not a spear at all, but ash wood with its bark on. Like Edward he called, 'Gissie, gissie,' he said, knowing the language from his own time. 'Come to me. Give me what is mine. Give me what the queen herself gave me to carry.'

He was bringing his hand between the boar's ears, scratching, scraping, with the nails of his left hand. The boar lifted its head, pleased with that. It sang a song of delight. Cuddy scratched its shoulders, and it hunched them against his hand.

Beyond them the clamour of the chase grew loud and immediate, and the low growth of the forest was broken where men and animals ran.

Then, from the intricacies of the stonework, Jude stepped clear, and stood for a moment, regaining her breath, smiling a smile of wickedness and joy complete. Behind her the hunt came to a stand, horns sounded with urgent signals, and men who were shouting were all at once sinisterly silent.

'Oh, it's Cuddy,' said Jude, thinking of running forward to him, then standing with one leg curved to a tiptoe, remembering what she had been for the last few minutes, ready

98

to run again.

Ange heard a noise, where someone trod the forest floor. A clicking noise followed. A creak like bending wood meant nothing to her.

Cuddy straightened his back and lifted something from the place between the boar's ears. He smiled, and began to speak.

'No,' said Jude, turning to look for what was coming, what had flown past her with a hissing whir. An arrow had come out of the silence, missing Jude, missing the boar. It had been aimed at both, because they had been one. The boar had come to Cuddy, while Jude took its place for the lord's hunt. But to change from being it she had had to come to it again, and brought the hunt with her.

The animal lifted itself away with a sky-filling squeal. It struck the table, and the candles toppled from their places, leaving darkness with streaks of sapphire blue light, more blinding than darkness.

The disturbance and noise changed to a flash of fire, an explosion, and daylight sudden and hard. The arrow strike had become gunfire in another place. The squealing screech of the boar turned into the haunting wail of an A10 anti-tank aircraft, manoeuvring above the moor.

Ange was with Ruth on the edge of Ancren Dale, under the thorn tree where hedgehogs lived. One was walking about now, nosing something.

The echo of gunfire was still in the air. There was a shout from Mum, who was now up on the moor. Dad was with her, looking over Ancren Dale. With him was another man.

'Hello,' Julian Westow was saying, out of cathedral uniform, in jeans and leather jacket, coming down to the thorn tree, picking something up. 'What's this?'

'There you are,' said Mum. 'You hadn't been gone long when

Julian came along with his father. So we came to fetch you. Are you all coming back for another tea? You took so much with you.'

'It got finished, that,' said Robin.

'Yes,' said Ruth, 'it did. The lot.' She frowned, as if she had forgotten some detail, or must have remembered wrong. 'All.'

Dad was saying, 'No peace, night or day, banging away on the tops here. That shell came near.'

The army fired again. Smoke crumped against the sky.

'What's the matter, Jude?' Mum was saying. 'You don't need to be frightened by the army.'

'They were chasing me,' Jude was saying, nearly in tears. 'They shot straight at us. It stung all over, and now he isn't here.'

'Who?' asked Mum.

'Our friend,' said Jude, very poutily.

Julian was gathering up what he had seen. He held the pieces out to Ruth. 'You'll know,' he said.

'Yes,' said Ruth. 'I understand now. It's the comb,' and she held up something made strangely of wood, with a brass back. 'And these,' she said, 'are the scissors.' She held them up by the loops of the handles. The blades, no longer dull with verdigris, reflected the bowed thorn tree. Of forest, chapel, boar, or Cuddy, this was the only sign. Mum, Dad, Julian's father, saw nothing but twigs and foolishness, and a hedgehog.

Jude held out her buttoned cardigan, folded to a cushion, and Ruth laid comb and scissors there.

'You were daft,' Ruth said. 'Getting hunted.'

'I'm the one that can do it,' said Jude.

Ange remembered an aftershadow of memory, the stricken boar falling, not into safety but back into the perpetual hunt, pursued for ever, for the whole of history. She had a quick strong anxiety about Beowulf, in case some such blow had come

100

to him, his history too private to withstand it.

The gun fired again, on the army's moor.

Beowulf was homesick for the forest. 'My own place,' he said. 'The forests of Durham are ready for hunting. Jude was very brave.'

'She *will* have to be,' said Elfrida. 'Until I died my bit of forest *was* prettier.'

'And', said Beowulf, thoughtfully, 'tastier. If I remember.'

'*That*', said Elfrida, 'unpleasantness was uncalled-for.'

'The Lord giveth,' said Beowulf's Christian part, 'the Lord taketh away. Amen.' And, he thought, it stoppeth her calling me by that name.

Elfrida double-counted beads, *rip*-rap, rip-*rap*.

Chapter Ten

'THOSE girls do it each year,' said Mum. 'Elizabeth, Stephanie, and Victoria, two of them so busy with good works they haven't time to gad about and get married, and looking after the third one, poor dear, so they'll want some children around now and then.'

Ange read the invitation again, the words floating on polished paper, not quite shiny. It was from Miss Norris, Miss S Norris, and Miss V Norris, Mr Cuthbert Norris and Colonel Sir Anthony Norris, to a grand Hallowe'en Party at Keld House.

'Midnight,' said Dad. 'I'll have to come and fetch you. Of course, it'll be All Saints' Day by then, so we might get home.' He gave the costly paper back, and left for work.

Ange put the invitation on her bedroom table and looked at it often. Ruth had one as well, and had replied. It was no trouble to her, but it took Ange an hour to plod through the desert of words, thanking each Norris lady, and each gentleman, by name, before being pleased to accept.

'They won't want me when they see this,' she told Mum. 'It looks as if Beowulf wrote it.'

'What a long way round the tummy you are,' said Mum, stretching out a tape-measure.

'You're tickling,' said Ange. 'And sticking pins in.'

'Just stop feeling them,' said Mum.

'I'll go on my broomstick,' said Ange.

'Your father keeps having that bright idea,' said Mum, squashily. 'But he hasn't your sense of humour. I'll sew for you,

you peel apples.'

'It's done,' said Ange, waving a magic needle, and going into the garden. Even my jokes are deaf, she thought.

In the middle of the fuss that Mum began to make about the matter, Jude walked in and stood waiting.

'If it isn't quite the right time I'll go away,' she said, when she heard a space between words.

'We were just going to peel apples,' said Ange.

'I'll do that,' said Jude, opening the drawer and finding a huge knife. 'If you do it in one piece you can be invisible.'

'I'll do it myself,' said Mum. 'Out, both of you, and don't fash me.'

They played hopscotch on the flags outside the garage, using Ange's chalks to mark out the beds. There was a raging sky overhead, yellow and blue, with twisting clouds. Jude gave up hopscotch when she seemed to be losing, and drew on the flags instead. Her reddish hair fell forward over her face, and in moving it away she streaked both face and hair with multicoloured chalk dusts. In shafts of sunshine through the tree branches she glowed now and then like a candle in that chapel in the woodland undercroft.

Her ugly little drawing could not be understood. 'You can't write small with chalk,' she said. 'I saw this at my Mum's work. They're right busy just now, those girls, my Mum making tea for them.'

The picture trailed its way from the gateway to the garage, where she had finished against the up-and-over door. She rattled the door a little with her rump against the painted panels, and the metallic thunder fell over her like a shower-bath of sound. The kitchen window rattled too, not as accompaniment, but to make her stop.

'I'm doing the sky,' she said, looking up into the real

atmosphere. 'Glishy, like I feel.'

Mum washed her chalk weather from her face before dinner time and sent her away. 'We'll be busy the rest of the day,' she said.

Jude walked away, rejected and offended.

'I think it will rain,' said Mum, looking out of the window when the sky darkened to a violet blue. She seemed pleased at the idea.

'Is it a good thing?' asked Ange.

'You know what he's like about drawing on the flags,' said Mum. 'But you did it before I saw.'

Ange scuffed the hopscotch beds a little before tea, but no rain came. Jude's drawings, she thought, were not even what infants do.

Dad came into the house in a strange mood, half angry, half excited. 'Has anyone been here?' he asked. 'A visitor?'

'No one,' said Mum.

They don't mean Jude, thought Ange. Do they?

'Anyone lurking about?' Dad continued.

'No,' said Mum. 'It hasn't rained, has it?'

'No,' said Ange. They were going to talk about Jude, she decided. 'I just did the outlines,' she said. 'With chalk. I didn't scratch the stones.'

Dad looked at her vaguely. 'You?' he said. 'You can't have done. You don't know how.'

'It'll wash away,' said Mum. A diamond of rain landed on the middle of the window, like a bullet, like an arrow. 'Jude did it all. All the rest.'

'Paper,' said Dad. 'It's all there to be written down. There's something wrong with that child, apart from her being wrong anyway.'

He brought himself paper from his study and went out again.

He stood outside between the beams of the car headlamps, and wrote what Jude had drawn, jot by jot, curlicue by curlicue.

'I don't know why she left off the beginning,' he said. For him the message started by the garage doors and went down, line upon line towards the road outside. 'It's the same thing, making sense but remaining nonsense because we have no historical background and no geographical background.'

'She started under the car,' said Ange, coming out and going in, slain by an icy raindrop at full speed dodging through the loose weave of the green cardigan and striking between the shoulder blades.

'She wrote it upside down?' said Dad, muttering to himself. 'Not knowing anything about the meaning. "His cup taken away and given to the pagan women, who transformed it into Ladywell beyond Yoadwath," that's the ford of the witches, wherever it is, "and here at a later time there was placed a stone marked with a cross, where the blessed saint himself had formerly first struggled with the Northman's god." Why, there's a hole in the manuscript here, look, she's actually drawn round the edge of it, where it has been burnt, and underneath are bits of words from the page below. Though what pigs have to do with it I do not know.'

The rain was washing chalk away now; but Dad had written to the foot of Jude's page.

'That's it,' he said, scribbling a few last characters down, the pencil going through wet paper. 'Mine will be unreadable too. Where did she see it?'

'Her Mum's work,' said Ange. 'I don't know where.'

'I'll go and ask,' said Dad. 'She can write down any more she knows.'

Mum knew that would be a hopeless idea, and that Mrs Fitch would be angry and embarrassed. 'She simply would not understand,' she said. 'Jude would end up in trouble. "Her head in my hand," her mother says, and she gets knocked about.'

'But this is a documentary source,' said Dad. 'History. I've got to know where it came from.'

'Leave it,' said Mum. 'You'll be history yourself if you don't get dry.'

'You've grown fatter,' said Mum, one particular evening after that. 'I can't get this round you. And that, miss, is the most unbewitching vest that ever thought it could go to a party.'

The hat disgraced itself by having a floppy point, no matter what was done.

'It's rather sweet,' said Mum, stiffened it up with a look. 'Like a little one-eared rabbit.'

'Don't fuss,' said Dad, because Ange was watching the slow clock hesitate to tell the truth. 'It's not far. I'll soon be home again.'

'I won't go in if it's only me,' said Ange. 'I won't. If it's only me don't stop. Don't start!'

Everyone paused for a moment because the telephone dinged. Mum had a mouthful of pins. No one was at the other end to ring again. Ange was heard something else as well. Out in the garden, or in her ear alone, another bell had sounded, once, twice, and a third time, no more.

But it was a signal, a call waiting, a start.

'You'll be all right,' Mum said. 'It should be nice. You'll be frightened. It's a Hallowe'en party. Don't forget to collect Ruth.'

In the car Ruth repainted Ange's face, because Mum had done pretty make-up, not horror.

They went in at the open door of Keld House, out of a dark night speckling with lazy snow, into a bright hall sparkling with golden picture frames, to be met by a servant in a neat dark dress, who was offering to take their coats and showing them where to go, with a lovely smile that was a greeting and a welcome, and truly meant.

'Of course I'm here,' said Jude. 'My Mum does all the tidying and I come up with her a lot. I know the whole house, so I'm the maid that lets people in. Then I get to come to the party this year. I'm old enough.'

'You look very nice,' said Ruth.

'I haven't changed yet,' said Jude. 'You wait. They made me real witch paint.'

Then she was giving the grave smile to a shortish hermit with a beard, but the active eyes and arms of Robin.

'I am Miss Norris,' said the jolly one of three ladies. 'This is Miss S Norris, and Miss V Norris.' Miss S was no good at smiling; Miss V had never done anything else, and never spoke.

The outside door pushed tight against its frame with a clothy sound. Ange saw from an undraped window snow hanging in the air, winter's dandelion-clocks telling winter's time.

Inside were more than the three Miss Norrises; there was old Colonel Sir Anthony, who sat by a fire drinking a fine drink from a crystal glass, uncle to the Miss Norrises and to Mr Cuthbert Norris. There was an exceedingly bony ginger cat. It rattled and creaked as it walked. Lumpy skin hurt the hand that stroked it. 'Bullets,' said Robin. 'Used to being shot.'

Ange knew Mr Cuthbert Norris. They shared another muddle about handshakes. 'We're so left-handed,' he said. 'It's a problem when we change our intentions in the middle.'

'You were a doctor,' said Ange. 'When I came with my ears.'

'You'd naturally bring them,' said Mr Norris. 'I do operations. You don't see people with rabbits' ears, do you? No. I've changed them to normal.'

Ange worked out the joke and smiled at it, then gathered up the moonstones round her neck. Witch she might be, but a woman needs a bit of decoration, she had told Mum. 'You could have pierced my ears,' she said, wondering if he would there and then put minute holes in the flop of her hat.

He remembered her, and what it had been about. 'You should have asked at the time,' he said. 'Though no one ever has.'

'Your uncle is the soldier,' Ange said, recalling the invitation. 'But you had a gun up there.'

'Weekend soldier,' he said. 'Territorial Army. Good fun.' Then he turned to Robin. 'I've been operating in your fields,' he said. 'Should have been rabbit pie tonight.'

The hermit shook his beard and wagged his stick.

Julian Westow was a lady witch, having an unladylike tussle with Robin about what was underneath.

Edward was in a long robe and a mathematical hat.

Miss Norris clapped her hands, stopping the music to bring everyone together for a game. Miss S, the severe sister, parted Julian and Robin, and lined people up. Miss V, smiling misleadingly, was put into a chair and given a sweet. She brought it out often and held it up to the light.

'She's handicapped,' said Jude, coming among the guests as a witch dressed in white. 'This?' she said. 'I told my Mum it was fancy dress, but she didn't listen.'

When the game started she was knocked out in the first round, and went to be angry against a curtain, gradually finding it was fun to be wrapped in the velour.

Later on she was with Ange again. 'I don't know the man,' she said. 'Only the old one. He's always here, supping brown wine, because he doesn't have to work. My Mum wishes she was like him, but she wouldn't know what to do with her time.'

'My Mum's always busy,' said Ange.

'Yes, I know,' said Jude, pityingly. 'She doesn't know how lucky she is. Anyway, these girls work. They do experiments. They've got a room.'

There were games, some for children, some for witches, and some collapsible conjuring from Colonel Sir Anthony, taking cloth sausages from his nieces' ears. Supper came later on. The food was strange, but not sausages. Crisps were in tiny bowls with spoons. You were meant to serve them out and eat them with meat that had soapy salt jelly all round it.

'Makes you thirsty,' said Robin. 'For plain water.'

Jude had a whole bowl of crisps. 'There isn't a pickled onion in sight,' she said. 'Dainties and niceties, and some nastities too. Don't touch them little green plums, they taste of toilet cleaner.'

Ange was not to be ordered about by the maid. She took an olive. The maid was right about the taste. Ange put the remains in her pocket.

Miss Norris came past then. 'Don't hide in the corners,' she said. 'Come out and enjoy the Treasure Hunt. There are clues to be found, and the others have started. We can't have all the cousins sitting together.'

The treasure was somewhere in the house, said Miss Norris, patiently wondering why children were so stupid.

'No need to go outside,' said Miss S Norris.

'Nice,' said Miss V Norris, without a sound, and held Miss S Norris's hand.

With the rules explained, they went away, leaving Mr Cuthbert Norris in charge. He had not been told what the treasure was or where it had been hidden.

A gate stood across the grand staircase, because that part of the house was private. 'I know the whole building,' said Jude.

'They've forgotten the back stairs near the kitchen.'

'It won't be up there if we aren't meant to go,' said Ruth.

'That's what they want you to think,' said Jude.

'If we're not meant to go there then the treasure won't be there,' said Julian. He peered up the stairs at strange small drawings framed on the wall, dragons and fraught cats, double-headed beasts, boars, troops of bears, insects tall as houses, lions in the wilderness, all real to the pen in some distant parchment day.

'I wouldn't go up to bed past them,' said Jude. 'We only get to use the kitchen stairs. They're not marked private so they're part of the house.'

At the top of the kitchen stairs a door opened to a corridor, and a landing beyond was carpeted. Party music and voices came to it up the big stairs. Smells of the Colonel's cigar and clean party dresses mingled with the pastryness of supper.

'They all sleep along here,' said Jude. 'That's the Colonel, this is the doctor one, and there's Miss V, look at all her toys.

The door of the room was open, the bed heaped with a bestiary of teddies and rabbits, rag dolls and golliwogs.

'I help her dress them,' said Jude. 'She's no good at it. This is Miss S, and at the end Miss Norris. She's a nurse. At the other end they do their experiments. The door's open. I'm allowed all over everywhere.'

They stopped over the threshold of the experiment room into twilight. A long table in the middle was heaped with jars, stands and dishes.

There were only three walls, of bare stone. Instead of the fourth lay a wintry landscape, snow coming in across the stone floor, surrounding the fire and melting before it. Grass bristled between flagstones, and on distant low hills trees grew like cracks in the sky. The shaky spars of a derelict roof criss-crossed grey cloud.

A crusted black ointment in a cauldron seethed lumpily, breathing like a death-rattle.

'Their worst potion ever,' said Jude. 'It's to make them fly. We aren't meant to see it. We'll go back.'

There was no exit now by the way they came in, no door in any walls. Yet they had certainly come through a doorway. Also, they had been followed.

Miss Norris, Miss S Norris, and Miss V Norris stood together and looked. The bony cat stalked about behind them, each footfall heavy. The noise of the party had vanished completely.

Miss V smiled at them knowingly. 'Nice,' she said. 'One of you knows where it is. Tell us.'

Miss S Norris nodded. Miss Norris beamed and said, 'We shall know in the end. Where is it?'

'Treasure?' asked Ruth. 'Have we won the game? Is it here?'

'That is a trinket,' said Miss V. 'You are here for another reason. The cup is important to us. We have not been able to find it, but we shall not let you do so. Tell us what you know.'

Ange recalled Dad's remarks when he stood on the flagstones outside the garage, writing down what Jude had drawn, or written, and saying occasional surprising words like Yoadwath, witches, and cups. Perhaps this was the time for those things.

Jude was quaintly pleased at seeing the Miss Norrises not quite as they had been. She liked a bad side to others.

Ange felt guilty. What was meaningless now had to be explained. She obviously looked guilty too.

'She knows,' Miss Norris shrilled out, unlike her jolly self.

'She will tell us,' said Miss S, a false and awful smile making her face uncomfortable.

111

'We shall find out,' said Miss V, confidently, stepping forward to grasp Ange.

Robin still had his stick. He rapped at Miss V's hand with it, and she let go. Ruth pulled, and Ange came away.

Edward hurled a heavy dish in the direction of the Miss Norrises. It bounded along the table, scattering jars and tools. Little creatures began to hop about among the tubes, jars and alembics.

Jude picked up a bundle and threw that. It burst, and writhing black shapes spread through the air. There was an angry shriek. Jude ran. 'They knew it was me,' she said to the others, already running out into the fully open air. 'My Mum won't work here any more after that. Sugar it.'

'We'd better go somewhere we know,' said Ruth, pulling Ange along. 'And then ring up home.'

'Those were snakes,' said Jude, happily.

Ange threw an angry slightly bitten olive.

They were in the snow, under that sky. Party pumps were the worst wear for snow, wet at once, cold, and feeling every harshness in the ground.

Behind them the three Miss Norrises attended to their table, gathering, ladling, housekeeping what went on in that room. One was always watching to see where Ange went.

Chapter Eleven

ELFRIDA scattered beads in agitation. 'Sometimes I can't follow the *simplest* prayer,' she said. 'Cuddy would have helped, but *you* don't.'

'Stranger things in the forest of my mind,' said Beowulf. 'Those are Norns, next thing to witches. We don't want them in charge. I would have gone with the girl, but she did not hear me.'

'A *wilful* child,' said Elfrida, 'one who does not listen. *Those* ladies will *not* want to lose the cup they hold. Even if they don't know it.'

Beowulf tensed himself. He induced gravity to think of him. He fell off the bed. 'Hold tight,' he said. 'If you are coming.'

Some time later Mum trod on him at the bottom of the stairs. She put him on the hall stand. Later still she came into the hall again, thinking she heard Daniel walking about, forgetfully going to bed without fetching Ange. There was no one there. Only a little snow had blown in through the slightly-opened door.

As Beowulf took her back in time, Elfrida told him more. 'Norns lay out the *lives* of children,' she said. 'Witches have taken *many* of their duties; but witches are now *fancy dress*.'

Ange looked back and saw the three Miss Norrises treading their way, looking eager. It was time to move.

Jude shivered. 'They're real witches,' she said. 'We're just party ones. Go a different way.'

'We must get back to the house,' said Ruth. 'We must be there at home time.'

'It's only playing,' said Jude. 'It must be. They're only messing about. It's more experiments. It'll be a potion.'

'Just move,' said Ruth briskly. 'Or get left behind.'

Jude thought she might like to be left, and was defiant for a moment. 'I'll come,' she said. 'For a bit. I can tell you want me.'

'We need you,' said Ruth. 'We did once, and we might again. We'll stay on this little path.'

The snow became softer. The path came to the edge of a little stream in the heather. A mist came up from the surface.

'Is it water?' said Ruth. 'If it's as dark as it looks we shouldn't be able to see it.'

Ange could see a long way through the water, to fields, roads, rivers, houses below. There were fires all across that landscape. Showers of bright sparks were rising and falling, and curtains of colour hung on the lower air.

Something leapt out of the moor they walked on, flung itself flaming into the air, tipped over, exploded in a starburst of gold, and faded on their vision with an empty sigh. An echo rattled among other clouds.

'Firework night,' said Jude. 'There'll be toffee down there.'

'We are on a cloud,' said Ruth, calmly. 'We must expect rockets to come up through it. Careful where you stand.'

The three ladies chuckled in delight at the rocket. Miss S made little jumps into the air, like a rehearsal for lift-off; Miss V said threatening prayers, the eldest, Miss Norris herself, started a slow incantation and a methodical dance. They were considering flight. The ginger cat sat on a gritty rock and looked down its nose.

The stream was now plain water, chattering and gulping to itself, rippling over stones and under edges, bubbles riding a black flow.

'Running water,' said Jude. 'Witches can't cross it.'

'Then you'll get left behind,' said Edward.

'I'm not a witch,' said Jude. 'But I've done experiments.' She shared her fancies as they walked along. 'I took some to school and did flying, and Sister Gabriel put the ladder up to get me off the roof.'

Ruth jumped Jude across the gap. Julian gave Ange a helpful punch, and she crossed too.

Beyond the stream three ladies began rubbing each other's backs, patting their own faces, massaging their legs, digging between their toes, poking behind their ears, slapping their bodies.

And going away without moving, Ange thought. But they had shrunk down to three small black creatures on the snow, hopping about like the things among the apparatus of the experiment room.

They were three black crows, calling harshly. When they had preened themselves thickly black as black, they flew. A stone stood up on four finger legs and walked stiffly about, a bad sign.

The birds had to fly round every branch and tributary, and up beyond the source, to find a way to the other side of the stream.

'We could go back,' said Ruth. But they had crossed cloud, and that is a one-way trip.

'We don't know where we are going,' said Edward.

'But I do,' said Ange. 'Jude told my Dad.'

'I know most things,' said Jude. But not this. 'What was it?'

'We have to cross Yoadwath and find a well,' said Ange. It wasn't very clear to her, heard from Dad in a funny mood on a rainy day. It had not been very clear to him.

'I remember,' said Jude firmly. Someone had to be in charge.

'We follow the path. I've been bringing you this way.' Perhaps she had, from the kitchen stair to here. 'Now you look after me.'

The ground began to sink and squash, and water came over their ankles. The path became a trail of mud straggling across a desolate green marsh tufted with reeds and matted with rushes.

A bird of the marsh gave a yelping cry, and another replied, as if a warning had gone out that witches had arrived.

Jude was right, and wrong. The witches were the fancy dress partygoers. The three Miss Norrises were something else.

'The Norns lay out the lives of *men*,' Elfrida explained, 'at its *source*, when they are born, and life runs like a river down the hill of time. They can alter it only then, *not* by crossing it later. And of course, *witches* may not cross running water *ever*. Are you listening, Bruin?'

'Not to you,' said Beowulf. 'Be quiet.'

'They leave no room for the work of *saints*,' Elfrida went on. 'When life is in the *cup* they rule that. Cuddy takes that cup and puts a different *meaning* into it. We *have* to be there first. They are pagans and *it* is a curse.'

Beowulf was tramping back to that time, bearish, shaggy. Details no longer interested him. 'Bears have been horribly cursed,' he growled. His voice had become toy-like over the years. He squeaked.

His first sin came to life, and was talking, *talking*, talking. Beads rattled. 'Faster, Bruin,' said Elfrida.

'I'm going as fast as I can,' Beowulf growled. 'There are traps and ambushes to watch for, as well as the sins of man and bear.'

'This is it,' said Jude, following her own thoughts and, as usual, being contrary about it. She distinguished a track where the others saw nothing. 'I'm trained,' she said. 'I got a good niff of potion in the experiment room.'

It was a poor path to follow, but the only one. 'It's very old,' said Jude, 'and forgetful.'

It avoided deep pools and went round sheets of quivering moss. It found its way to a road of flat stones lying under still water.

Perhaps this was Yoadwath, the ford of the witches. 'Look for a cup,' said Ange, because the cup lay beyond Yoadwath.

'Cup?' said Jude. 'We want a blooming boat.'

The path gave out. The wilderness of marsh had overtaken it both ahead and behind.

Three crows were in the air, and had got to the far side of the ford. They called with a mocking laughter, sure that time would give them power. Perhaps they thought they could not be seen.

Jude no longer knew which way to go. They dared not cross, they dared not take another pace.

They stood in a green and slimy place, and the marsh began to smell particularly bad. There was no way forward, and no path behind.

'Bowking,' said Jude, when the marsh belched.

Bubbles broke and popped. To match their noise a small bluish flame, hardly visible itself, but giving a faint light to stems and leaves, stood reflected on open pools, and drifted slowly away.

'That is Cuddy's fire,' said Elfrida. 'Fire was always *close* to him. It is the sign of a great saint. Be *there*, Bruin. Let us *be* there.'

'We follow that,' said Edward. The bobbing light led them knee-deep in quagmire, and in streaky canals beside thickets of water-

117

trees. Three crows watched from the air, waiting.

The bubbly light came into clear running water and expired. Water moved against legs, and washed away the muds and strands of peat. They climbed up on land and felt they had got somewhere.

'I'd like to be back at the party,' said Jude. 'All this walking isn't why I came to it.'

There was more walking. The path still led them, beside a river swift in its broad bed, too wide to jump, too deep to wade.

The bright moon dazzled them when they saw it again round a curve. Three shadows were three crows straddling the path. They had completed a journey round. The ginger cat had come his own way to join them. They waited.

It was very kind of them to bring party food out here to their guests. They had laid it out on neat tables beside a vigorous fire, and waitresses were holding chairs for them to sit on; and the party going on without them so sadly, just beyond.

'Oh, I don't know,' said Jude, doubtfully, spoiling things for everyone once again. 'Them sarnies, they won't keep still. It's that experiment table again.'

'Oh Jude,' said Ruth. 'They are being so kind, and we have been very thoughtless.'

But it's strange, Ange thought, that the cake has toadstools moving on it, and the trifle is festering, and the drink has gone bad. Also the party sausages had put out eyes on long stalks and begun to slither about leaving slimy trails.

And the noise the food made, squealing and yelping, hideous laughter among curranty things, hiccuping cheers from the pastry, and shrill howls from bowls of fruit (or caterpillars?).

Ange could make the meal nice or horrid, could almost see what she liked. But not quite.

118

Robin was holding a maggot fat and large, looking for a tasty dip, until it spoke, and kissed his hand.

Edward, in his plain way, kicked the table and found that his foot went through it, that it was not there, and that it vanished.

Three ladies stood in the moonlight, ready to gloat about finding what they had lost.

'We'd better go,' said Robin, shaking off the maggot. 'Leave, escape.'

Ruth was wondering quite how unmannerly they had been. And the three ladies were being so very forgiving.

Jude was having a much better time. She had seen a friend. Cuddy was on the river, bringing logs on a raft, like a passenger bringing luggage. The raft was poled along by dark men.

'They came with the Romans,' Cuddy was saying, 'to work the Tyne and the Wear, boatmen from the Tigris river, near Babylon, the Garden of Eden close by, where we all began, which some call Paradise or Neorxenawang.'

There was no mistaking his reality. The ladies were now like tree stumps hollow and brittle with age. But Cuddy was sitting on real logs, Jude reaching out a hand to him, Cuddy reaching out a hand to each of them in turn. The boatmen were watching, keeping the raft steady.

Under the water the flagstones of Yoadwath were square.

Then Edward was helping Ange off at the far side of the water, and they were all dry, and comforted as if they had been fed.

The ladies, left behind again, awoke. Once more they rubbed each other's backs, spreading their black ointment. But this time the crows could not fly, and only ran about with folded wings, angry with one another and scolding the ginger cat.

It was not so easy to stay away the next time. There was a

wooden trestle bridge, pretty like a picture, ready to cross, wanting to be crossed. It stood on four pillars across the water, safe and steady. They came to it by following a path, a thing you cannot help doing once you have begun to trust it; this one had been a good servant.

They looked across and saw the lights of Keld House. They heard the singing, and knew there would be warmth and food, journey's end, and that this was sure to be true.

'We've done enough,' said Ruth. 'You all ought to be safe across there. Go across. Whatever it is, it's over.'

'Yes,' said Jude, but doubtfully. Beyond the bridge the three Miss Norrises beckoned and smiled, innocent again.

'Cars will be coming for us,' said Robin.

It was Julian, rather to one side, who drew in his breath when he understood what the bridge was, who made it, and what from.

The bridge lifted one of its back legs and scratched itself behind the ear, as ginger cats do.

'Stop that, Beowulf,' said Elfrida. 'I like it. What *are* you doing?'

'Laughing,' said Beowulf. 'Poor pussy fell in the water. No harm, I think, in the occasional lop. Fleas come in handy.' He was hunkered down in the snow, stretching a leg and having a great scratch. 'Like old times,' he said. 'Could do with a snack, mind. But this is great. Haven't had a lop since I don't know when.'

'Just be *rid*,' said Elfrida. 'And it's *not* just you getting scratched.'

On the hilltop stood a heap of rock. It was once a building. The shape had now almost gone, but the spring it had been built round still bubbled and sang, water tumbling from a small

120

fissure.

A stone bowl caught it and dropped it evenly from its edge. Water was spun into silver sheets that tore to tatters before they hit the grass below. Frost sparkled, and scales of ice glittered. Smoke rose from the bowl, scented far away with the incense of the moon.

The path led here, high beyond Ancren Dale, beyond the shepherd's hut and Yoadwath, to the first snows of winter, where moonlight was almost warm.

'This is the Lady's well,' said Robin.

'Which lady is it?' asked Edward.

'All of them,' said Ange, dipping her fingers in. The water made the fingers the degree colder that frosted her blood and glaciered her bones. With the other hand she held a stone standing tall and firm as a doorpost.

Jude pulled up her sleeve, put her hand deep into the water, and brought out a dark metal cup, a goblet, with a stem. 'Freezing daft,' she said, holding it up, tipping out the water.

Bird claws scraped on the fallen rocks. Under the orb of the moon the crows were back, cocking their heads, watching. They began to be three ladies.

Water spilled from the basin, and light spilled from the sky; but it was a wooden sky full of heated air.

Ange's hand held the same stone, now forming the doorway of a cupboard-like room. The bowl was an earthenware sink, and water trickled leakily into it from a brass tap.

The high moor still showed through the walls of the room until they drew themselves solid and all that other place was cut off.

Jude held a cup of dark metal, harder and thinner than lead, with a stem like a goblet.

'Oh, don't use that tap,' said Mr Cuthbert Norris, passing

the scullery between the kitchen and the back stairs. 'We don't drink from that old spring any more. Not up to EC standards.'

Ruth held the dull cup on its waisted leg. It was dry from lying in its cupboard. Round its rim paced the pattern they already knew. In it were watery crystals, but not of frost. It was used for household purposes, and during flower arranging at the cathedral. Ange had sipped from it there.

'We wouldn't have seen it without going all that way,' Ruth said. 'They didn't, and they live here and they've had it all the time.'

'This is the back scullery and the servants' sink,' said Jude. 'My Mum empties the pails down it. That's the soda measure. It's wetty stuff.'

'Good hunting, hey?' said Miss Norris, passing along the corridor with her sisters, touring the party. 'Don't drink the water, you know.'

'The treasure still isn't found, Judith,' said Miss S.

Ange nearly said that it was, and her face went red from foolishness just avoided.

Miss V smiled her empty smile that meant 'So nice', and touched Jude's head as they passed.

'She used to be the best one,' said Jude, puzzling about a different impression. 'I expect she still is.'

'We won't go up, Judith,' said Ruth, looking at the small back stairs beside the kitchen. 'They don't want us up. We didn't go. Did we?'

'I often go,' said Jude. 'Miss V has all these dolls, and the Colonel snores in the afternoon.'

The cat sat upright at the top of the flight, on the last of the drugget. It shook its head, and kicked an ear where something moved.

'It's the cup,' said Ange. 'Same as the bell is the bell, and the stick is, and the comb and scissors thing. What next?'

From the big room came a shout and the clapping of party-goer hands, as the party treasure was found.

They spent the rest of Hallowe'en keeping warm, until the party was over and the transport of All Saints' Day came for them.

'Pumpkins for ever,' said Dad.

'So nice,' said Miss S, sternly seeing guests off at the door; Jude fetching coats; the weather blowing in; Miss V being sent to bed but floating about the landing in a nightie; Sir Anthony sleepily still sipping brown wine; Ruth sitting in the front seat of the car like Mum; vortices of snow running up the lamplight into their eyes; at home Beowulf cold on the stairs, smelling of swamp and chilblains beginning deep inside.

Chapter Twelve

'LIKE a stretcher,' said Edward. 'Long handles sticking out at each end. You should take them off if you put the box down, but I've had to screw them to the sides.'

Ange had looked in at the yard of the Swan Inn for a moment, coming with Mum to the shop. Edward showed her pieces of wood, with nothing joined to anything. It was his Craft, Design, and Technology so he knew what he was doing.

'Everybody keeps interfering,' he said. He gave a look of despair towards his own family twins, and their minder, Jude. 'We put in a new bar floor, so this is oak off the old one. I got the nails out, and planed it down so it isn't flavoured of beer any more. Hard as bone, right old.'

The wood looked new, except where iron nails had rotted in it over the years.

'It was squarer,' said Ange. She knew exactly what he was making, because she had seen it on Merrylaw, though not close-to. She did not like to think of it. 'You could lie down in it.' She specially did not like to think about that.

'There's no need for that,' said Edward. 'But I can't get at the work. Jude doesn't help; *she* isn't looking after *them*, only playing with the tools; and they're ganging up on me.'

'Electric screwdriver,' said Jude. 'Magic.' She slotted pieces of wood together, dropped screws into their holes, whizzed them in with the machine, then whizzed them out again.

Ange was jealous. 'We haven't got one of those,' she said. 'We probably don't need it.'

'We've got a bigger one,' said Jude, inventing it on the spot.

Ange ended with Jude at home. There was nowhere else for her, Jude said. Her house was bleak and empty, curtains dangling across dirty windows.

Jude was about to teach Beowulf and sat him on a white insulator in Ange's corner of the garden.

'We should only ask for things once.' Cuddy was talking to visitors but allowing Ange to hear. 'I asked you twice for a beam of wood of a certain size. No, do not be sorry, because I was wrong to ask even once for anything to make matters better for me. I now understand that. I had only to walk round the island to find it, at first light seeing how my birds and my seal-folk were faring. The tide brought in a long black spar of wood from the depths of the sea. I knew what it was, and I thought of you brothers, and forgave you.'

'It's for his toilet,' said Jude. 'To stop him falling in the sea. Go on, Cuddy.'

'Toilet?' said Ange. 'How do you know? He didn't say it.'

'You get the radio of it,' said Jude. 'I get television. He's showing them a piece of wood, stuck in the rocks. The sea comes underneath, so he doesn't even have to flush it.'

Then Cuddy was discussing his garden. 'Even here,' he said, 'little mice eat the barley. If I could catch them you could take them back to the mainland, where there is all they need.'

'It's like a carpet,' said Jude, as if she saw a real garden. 'All in and out and overlapping.'

'Hush,' said Ange. 'He hasn't finished.'

He talked about turning back the slugs by hand to live on the seaweed they could eat and he could not. 'They are awake as soon as I am,' he said. 'How do I know they are not saying their prayers before me, and with equal right?'

'He doesn't mind the rain,' said Jude. 'But the others do.'

Ange did not know there was rain. She heard one voice clearly, and others even less than the radio in the kitchen, which was now having a fit of the news after spitting out the pips of the time signal.

Cuddy, having shown his visitors where white gulls lay on a whitened rock – Ange heard their noise very loud – took them somewhere indoors. Ange felt the rain fall from his voice, and relief come into his visitors'.

'The greatest gift of warmth is after cold,' said Cuddy. 'We must take care not to enjoy being warm, or we want more: we must always praise cold for being so strongly its own nature.'

'It's a fire,' said Jude. 'It's dinner. He hasn't eaten anything all the day, and he's been cooking them dinner without telling them. I think it's a turkey. Special, anyway.'

'It is not because you are a king,' Cuddy was saying, 'but because there is a goose. Three or four days ago fishermen from down the coast caught it in their net. They do not think it worth eating, but all the same it is a gift from God. And onions grow well here. It is the salt, I say. Each one is a meal for me. Too much eating makes me dizzy, and barley takes my senses away.'

'There isn't a crown,' said Jude, thinking of the king. 'There's nothing on his head but hair. Cuddy's hair has all fallen off at the front. My Dad's has fallen off all over, but he's quite handsome.'

The conversation on the island became difficult and probably private. Ange did not understand it, and thought she ought not to listen.

Jude switched off her pictures, and went back to teaching Beowulf. He was just stupid enough about sums to keep her occupied.

'We used to do sums,' said Elfrida. 'One of the sisters could do some terrible stuff in her *head*.'

'One day, one meal, that's all I know,' said Beowulf.

'Sometimes you *share*,' said Elfrida. 'That's division. How would you manage *that*?'

'That's the other bear's problem,' said Beowulf.

Cuddy and his visitors went outside. There was one more thing to show them.

'It catches rainwater now,' said Cuddy.

'But it's stopped raining,' said Jude. 'No, Beowulf, you will have to write it again. It's a lovely night, all yellow sky.'

The visitor said, 'And in the end will it catch your soul?'

Cuddy laughed. 'Perhaps it is too large,' he said, 'for a small spirit. It was sent to me by a dear friend.'

'What is it?' said Ange. 'They can see it so they aren't saying.'

'It's a bed,' said Jude. 'No, it's a bath. It's got water in. There's a place for your head. Oh no, it's a big stone grave. It's where he's going to die and be buried. They'll have to empty it first. Sit up, you naughty bear. Look, did you see, Beowulf wraggle his ears very cheekily.'

The visitor was being taken away in a boat. Cuddy walked beside it, helping it to the deep tide that set for the shore.

The king reached out a hand and took Cuddy's fingers, raising the circle of gold that spanned one of them.

'Bless me, father,' he said. 'Kingdom is all temptation. Help me to choose right.' He raised Cuddy's hand to his lips. Against the flashing sunset a spark glowed red in those fingers. The boat was away then, dark as the waves, up and down in them, the oars seeking water.

Cuddy turned and sought his island.

Jude considered matters. 'I've been keeping an eye on him,' she said. 'He hasn't got that ring these days. I've held his hand, so I know. But I saw it on his finger just now. The king kissed it.'

'Oh,' said Ange, looking into the empty but echoing bell. 'I said he would give me a ring, but I haven't got it yet.'

'If you know what to do,' said Jude, 'then you only have to do it.' She gave Beowulf a hard look with a pointing finger, meaning a tricky point in two-add-two for him. 'So that's the next thing.'

'We are the ones that should know,' said Ange. 'I wish I could ask him.'

'He doesn't know he's lost it,' said Jude. 'We'll look in Ancren Dale.'

Ange was reluctant to be responsible for Jude.

'I think I'll come up with you,' said Mum.

'You can look after the tea,' said Jude. 'Last time some pig ate it all up, and the basket as well.'

'We'll just take biscuits for a snack,' said Mum, assuming that Jude was complaining about the boys and exaggerating about the basket.

'We don't actually need you,' said Jude to Mum. 'You needn't worry. We'll meet the shepherd and be quite safe.'

'Then so shall I,' said Mum. 'Don't worry about me.'

No one walked in Ancren Dale but themselves. Sheep took no notice. All was so quiet and still that Ange heard the grass tearing as it was grazed and swallowed.

Mum saw the white cat. It walked through the grass, considering its own affairs.

'Ts-ts-ts-ts,' she said, speaking cat language. The cat gave her a nod, said the same back, and went on its way.

'Be like that,' said Mum. 'Meow.'

The white cat said nothing more. It knew where it was going.

'There might be white kittens in the rocks,' said Ange.

Jude and Ange followed it. It made its way solemnly up the slope under the neb of Chapel Stack. It looked back at the corner. It leapt in a dignified way up the rock face, found a place where a squared boulder had fallen away, turned itself round, and lay down. With its chin on its forepaws it looked out over Ancren Dale.

'There's all sorts of places,' said Jude. 'This is like a cave I can get in, except it stops.'

'There's a deep one here,' said Ange, putting her hand into darkness, 'but it's too small for me.'

The white cat still lay flat, watching the distance, peering through the treetops rising from houses the far side of the valley. It was no longer looking over Ancren Dale.

'It looks different,' said Jude, seeing the change too.

Ange was uncomfortable. 'We'll go and get a biscuit,' she said, turning round and following the path, wide and gravelly to reach Mum. 'We can come back another time.'

Jude said flatly, 'There wasn't a path when we came.'

The path was a sloping ledge. Below it trees grew and a river showed an oily gleam, ripples reflected a grey sky and houses the far side.

Above the path rock showed, bare and heavy. A ledge or two up the white cat licked a foot between searchings of landscape. It was now sitting on the sill of an archway in a stone wall hugely high.

An iron grille was the door to a cave that was part natural, and part artificial. It had raw rock to one side, built wall to the other, and the floor ran up in sand towards the back. The cat waited for them inside.

'We'll never get them,' said Jude, intent on kittens. 'We can't get through that gate. The holes are too little.'

Someone walked down the path. He stopped and spoke. 'I

didn't know you were here,' said Julian Westow.

'Stop mucking about,' said Jude. 'It's you that's here with us, not us there with you. We're on the moor. Getting kittens.'

'I'm on my way to a music lesson,' said Julian, beside his own cathedral, carrying a thin case. 'That's the cathedral cat. It never has kittens because it's a tomcat. It's called St William of Carileph, and the cathedral buys it food. That's just a drain, and it'll be catching rats.'

Ange and Jude stared at him wildly, knowing he was very likely right, but wrong as well. 'Is there a key to go through the gate?' Ange asked.

'I don't know,' said Julian.

'It's the ring,' said Jude. 'That's what we've come for.'

'I'll be late for my lesson,' said Julian walking on.

'Mum's here,' said Ange. But it was a hope, not a certainty. A strange sensation was creeping over her, as if her skin tightened. Her clothes seemed to be pulling away, and the sky darkening. This is just a different way of feeling sick, she decided, and wondered where it would happen.

It was not that. The clothes were in a heap, and she was under them. They were heavy, and crushing her, and she crawled out from under the weight.

'What are they doing?' said Beowulf.

'*Dear* St William,' said Elfrida. 'This is when Cuddy had a problem with an *infestation*.'

'Lops again,' said Beowulf. 'We've done that.'

'Not *fleas*,' said Elfrida. 'Something bigger.'

Ange came out from under her skirt and stood on the ground. Grass was tall around her, and her clothes heaped up like a huge unmade bed, skirt, T-shirt, green cardigan, something pink, and

130

a spread-out sock. The toes of two shoes poked out from the heap. She climbed up on one to look for herself, knowing she could not be down on the ground, that herself must have vanished.

Another heap of clothes moved a little, because of what was inside it, a cautious gingery muzzle, black beads of eyes, ears both rounded and pointed, and teeth like white needles. It drew its long length out, turned round, and sniffed the clothes. It crossed the ground with arched back, and went through the iron grille. It looked back and waited for Ange, tawny to the tip of its tail.

Ange had a long tail, smooth grey fur, and hands with little claws. She knew she was a mouse, and that Jude was a hedge creature that ate mice. She would have dived for her clothes again, but they were a long way off in the open. Beyond the bars, inside the cave, were small safe corners.

She knew what Jude was. One had once been seen on the playground wall. Jude was a weasel, from head to tail, every hunting dangerous inch. The weasel stood up on its hind legs and looked about.

The cat watched them both, patiently, not losing its calm; being always unruffled, like Ruth Obley.

The throat of the cave closed on them. First the nearly-useful rubbish of cathedral workmen: planks, lengths of rope, a hammer-head, a sawblade; all so big they were like statues to Ange, to a mouse.

Then there was a ragged crack ahead, with a floor where they could walk. Some forks in the road were not left or right, but up or down. They went upwards when they had a choice. Behind Ange the weasel stalked, not threatening, but alarming, bound to want to eat, and to do it, first kill. Ange breathed hard weasel smell, like a man's den in the cab of a lorry, bitter and aromatic.

St William of Carileph paced slowly. He chirruped when Ange began to creep along a hole too small, deep in the world's rock. He knows all the ways, thought Ange. She obediently found another path.

She came out of nature's realm and into man's. Stone round her now had been cut and placed, set in mortar, and built. Dry sand shifted under her paws, and once a black beetle taking its own walk. She wished she could understand why it was getting itself eaten, but that was what it did, brittle and fat, bristly legs moving in her mouth.

The weasel held itself back. The cat turned away.

Slow muttering throbs in the walls came closer, shaking the fabric a little, the footsteps of people above, coming and going.

A shaft of light stood across her way. She looked up at greenness and carved stone a long way off. Dusky colours walked.

She got up close under the hole, climbing and holding. She put her head out, and then an arm, or foreleg. She was out, standing on a paving-stone, glad that being a mouse was over. In a moment she could be rescued and sent home: she need only tell her story to be taken away and comforted.

She went to a lady who looked kind and liked children because she had a lot of them with her. She spoke, but was not heard. She tapped the lady on the shoe.

'Sister Gabriel,' said a child's voice, 'you got a rat on your shoe.'

Ange knew she had again met something like a wolf in the trees. She ran from it at once. There was a foot over the hole she had come through, so she ran another way. Children shrieked with excitement.

The white large shape of St William of Carileph came to

132

check that all was well. He was upon her at once, a huge paw clamping her tail down, the other cupping and holding her, blocking her escape.

His mouth came down open, and teeth like spears closed round her and picked her up, his Tom to her Jerry.

Ange expected points like a garden fork to plunge through her, scraping on bone. The teeth were holding but not biting. Her heart stopped while the cat ran off with his catch, and in her whole body nothing happened.

The cat then walked solemnly along a stone floor. He growled, to show someone who owned what. A voice said, 'Good boy, let it go,' and someone held out a hand. St William offered it a bloody handshake and it went away. Teeth and tongue arranged Ange comfortably again. They pushed her firmly. The walls of the throat rippled, and swallowed her alive into warm darkness.

There was nothing to breathe. Ange was churned about, like being caught in bedclothes that are tying themselves up, stretching and twisting at hot midnight. She struggled and kicked in this nightmare.

St William of Carileph, sitting on the cloister roof, overlooking a little square of green grass, put his head over the edge, and sicked her up into a gutter just below. Grey rain was falling.

She saw a dry hole in the stonework, and went into it, damp but alive, quite unhurt, but breathing as if she had run up to the roof rather than being carried. St William followed across the leads. The mouse heard him breathe at an opening in the mortar, listening for her heart to beat louder.

She scuttled through cracks and crevices, knowing Jude had been this way, without knowing how she knew, as a mouse thinks.

Jude was round a corner suddenly, rushing out to make a kill, before recognition prevented her. She wrinkled her weasel nose and let Ange go past.

Ange led the way. She came across a thick yellow cylinder of soft rich stuff, and had to eat it. Jude went away among the stones. A distant call of despair emerged from a hapless creature, and in a little while Jude was back, licking her whiskers. She had a good wash with her tongue, and seemed happy to wait for Ange to finish her meal of ripe tallow candle, mature as aged cheese.

Chapter Thirteen

ANGE found her way, without knowing where she had to go. Once she came out into the open air, on a narrow road made of a single huge stone, high and overhanging, and far below a procession walked in an emulsion of colours from flaring windows lit by a setting sun.

The people below knelt. Many were in white. One stood beside a table, and another sprayed him with smoke from a golden bowl on a golden chain. The smell was like the strangest take-away, newly opened from an unknown country.

Ange and the fearsome Jude went down the hollow centre of a pillar, round and round the filler stones, and under the floor again, while choir and organ thundered above.

Afterwards silence stood solid. An open archway showed the aisle of the cathedral. The people went away; the sweet smoke settled on the dust. Doors banged, and keys were turned in locks. Darkness leaked into the building from outside; the windows dimmed themselves soft, and slept.

Luminous in the mist paced a white cat. St William of Carileph had his high church to himself and came to make his peculiar prayers. He lifted his head, ruffed like a lion's, and spoke one word to the bay where Ange and Jude rested.

Jude showed her needle teeth. Perhaps it was a smile, perhaps not. Ange knew she must move now. What was ahead drew her forward, and the presence of Jude behind her drove her on.

Jude followed through untrimmed stone. They were deep in

stonework now, and the feeling of the place changed. Ange hesitated, not wanting to go further, aware of intruding uninvited where she had no right to visit.

Beside her Jude arched her back, thrusting her head forward and then withdrawing it, alarmed by what she too did not know.

Even a mouse may sense its lack of quality, its unworthiness; and a weasel by being larger and wilder can sense it more. The mouse that was Ange could not approach what she was being measured by. After all, it had to be greater than her, or it could not judge her.

But if she turned and went she knew she would remain as she was, in only part of her life. And it would be a short part, as pure mouse, with Jude following quickly as pure weasel. She would have failed. They would both have failed.

She stood and could go no further. What lay ahead was too holy. She was in a darkness that was not complete because she had the senses of a mouse; and because the way forward was into a greater light of all the senses, better but dreadful.

In the darkness moved a whiteness that she knew. St William of Carileph came into the rough stonework, easing his way through alleys and clefts truly too narrow for an old cat half priest from age and attention to duty; he who could have sung the services all year, preached every sermon, said every lesson; been bishop.

He too was shy as he moved forward, with Ange able to move in his shelter, Jude in his shadow. He murmured small apologies and loving remarks, to them and to someone else.

Ange knew him for a small saint, and that ahead of them was a greater one. She listened for words, for a bell, for a sign to tell her who was here.

They came into a room under the ground, with the sound of feet moving on a floor above. In the middle of the room was an oblong wooden box. From it came the power that filled her with dread and doubt, and that wanted to fill her with joy if she knew how to let it.

Jude whimpered, frightened at being shown to truth. St William of Carileph bowed his head, and his thick white coat stuck close to him as if it had grown wet.

At once, but as if it took a whole day for her to realize, Ange sensed that she had come to a familiar place. Here was the shepherd, here was Cuddy, and she was close to him. His own real presence was like light in the way it shone, and like time in its iron-like firm grip.

But it was Cuddy, and only Cuddy. She had seen him as a boy, as a man, striving to find heaven.

Jude came forward, low and fearful. It was not an alarmed fear, but a respect she had not come across very much, the attention that visits if you are truly hurt, with perhaps a broken leg, and cannot move, but are loved. Jude was often broken but rarely loved.

Ange felt the world's hurts being taken away for both of them. You have lived with your hurts long enough to rely on them, so taking them away causes pain that is a delight and a torment at the same time, like cutting a tooth.

The many-toothed weasel could not shake away its helplessness. Jude could not speak, but looked at Ange; and Ange understood her eyes.

Here was Cuddy, both alive and dead, just as he had been in life, spare and light, frail and complete. Here he had been laid, and here he had given blessings to the miserable and hurt for a thousand years. But this was not where he wished to be. Another part of him, neither body nor soul, searched for a resting place between heaven and earth.

For the traveller to go to that resting place, his Paradise, his

Neorxenawang, his island again, another relic had to be recovered and help complete him.

It had been on Mum's list, but the mouse could not remember much at all. Jude knew, as if she had done it before. But Jude could not move, too overcome by feelings she had not met before.

Overhead in the cathedral a bell harshly jangled a summons to prayer, and a scary plainsong service began, with voices like spears.

Elfrida had heard something of the sort in Cyprus. 'They *sang* there,' she said. 'That was lovely *religion*. Like the old days.'

'It was good on honey,' said Beowulf. 'If they left any. And there was a whole machine made of bones. Alive. It happens.'

'They're not getting on at all *well*,' said Elfrida. 'They haven't been *brought up* to it.'

'They're young too long,' said Beowulf. 'Along the way they forget nearly all they're told.'

Overhead the singing grew louder and wilder, as if wolves were running in the forest.

Another voice belonged to Jude, not brave enough to carry out the task she had come to do. Cheek and confidence had left her, and she called for help. Cuddy tried to reassure her, to tell her that she was setting out to do what was right, and that it was her duty, in spite of Cuddy's complaint. But Jude was afraid to go on and too ashamed to turn back. She curled up and tried to sleep, or possibly die.

St William of Carileph stood up. He turned his eyes full on Ange and stared. His mouth opened and closed. He might have said a prayer, or that it was a nice day, and Ange wanted to reply and help the weasel, but was herself too afraid to turn away, too abased to go forward in that unshaded and unusual light. There must be better people, she was sure, and one of them should take over.

St William of Carileph came to her with a dribbling purr. He ran his tongue over her, from nose to tail, flattening her ears with its rough sharpness, making them sing, wrapping her ribs to her back, and tingling the length of her tail.

Jude whimpered. In the top of the vault a grating noise began, and a crack of deep yellow light slowly grew larger.

What she would do for Beowulf, Ange realized, she would do for Jude. But she is never going to sleep on my bed. If I think of her as Beowulf . . .

But it was Jude she must help. To do it she made a list of the awfulness of Jude, and threw it away line by line, the smell, the clinging persistence, the moodiness, the rage, the selfishness, the inability to lose without causing a storm, always saying what would upset or shock, of hating, of being bossy. The list was not Jude's fault, and Ange let it all go, item by item, now Jude was stilled into being what was behind all that, a terrified creature.

Ange saw her backed up against the wooden wall, her mouth open in a frozen grin, her weasel tail coiled stiff, her claws tense, as if she had withered and become rigid in a long frost.

She was like Beowulf in having fur, like Beowulf in lying unresponsive on the bedroom floor out of reach when he was needed, cold in the light of dawn, not always wanting to be picked up and made a fuss of or be useful.

Ange stroked the side of Jude's head, between jaw and ear, feeling bone under the fur, until Jude's grimace relaxed, softened, and became part of the smile that she wore for fright and uncertainty.

Jude uncurled again. Her forefeet touched the floor again. Her back flattened. She chattered to Ange, in her sharp unthank

139

way, and moved into the wooden box, through one of the patterns carved into it.

Ange grew content. I could stay here, she thought, at the foot of Cuddy's bed, because he is here, like the dolly for Jesus in the Nativity Play, alive for that performance, alive for this. She felt with her own paws the incisions of the pattern, but needed light to see them.

Overhead in the vault of the room, light was increasing in a square opening, and she saw the figures ranged along the wood. Behind the wood, in Cuddy's box there was noise. Cloth was torn roughly, pulled at with teeth and claws, dug out, unwrapped. Sweet smells spread, of herbs, wine, of holy comfort.

A struggle and striving began. After an angry chirrup from the weasel, and a last kicking tug, a small metallic object hit a wooden floor, rolled a little, and lay still.

It was not still for long. The weasel tipped and shoved and scraped it about, because it was difficult to pick up. It was edged to a corner, where it tapped once on each wall, and stayed in the angle until it was levered up and lifted.

Jude came out from where she had been. Light from the open trapdoor showed what jewel hung from her mouth and made it shine red.

Ange, wondering why Jude was greeting her nose to nose, lifted her front feet from the ground to return the greeting.

The greeting was Jude's plan. As noses touched what she carried slid from the weasel's mouth, over the mouse's head, round Ange's neck, hard, cold, metal with a bitter smell, heavy as a tree, pushing her to the ground again. It was tinkling and turning, rolling her with it across the stone floor. But it still stayed round her neck. She was captured by it.

When Ange had worked her way out into the vault again

Jude was running by the wall. Light seeped in overhead, and people were looking down with dark faces. The square of light went away with a bang.

Jude went away too. St William of Carileph had gone. Ange was alone, encumbered by the heavy collar that dragged her neck down and knocked against her feet as she walked.

It impeded her very much all along her route back. She followed Jude's quick footsteps, clear on stone all the way, distinct in their flavour, plain as light.

At last a rosy evening wandered through treetops beyond the iron bars at the cave-mouth. Jude waited at the entrance, watching and listening. She bent to sniff at Ange when she came near.

I do not trust her, thought Ange, not judging Jude, but knowing that nettles sting without blaming them for it. Jude went through the bars, and Ange followed. The metal round her neck chinked on the iron. A passing person turned a head and looked.

The ground outside was dark, without colour. Ange saw a heap of clothes and realized she should be in them. She ran to them, wanting to be herself again, covered and safe.

She hesitated, not knowing which were hers and which were Jude's. Putting on Jude's clothes and wearing them next to her own skin would be worse than staying a mouse for ever.

Her garments were heavy as she burrowed into them. Then they were closely on her and she felt them no more. She was herself, only, sitting alone under the wall of the cathedral, feeling the day's stored sunlight shining out of it.

The weight had gone from round her neck, but she felt sick, or worse, with her gullet completely blocked in a painful way. From the twitch in her throat she knew awful things must happen. She put her hand to her throat and her mouth opened.

Her tongue curled from its root.

A hardness was squeezed from her throat. She assumed it was a vital life-bone out of place, and tried to swallow it. With a sudden coughing throw of her whole body a gold ring with a red stone jumped from her mouth, sparkled in the sunset, and scampered down the bank on to the path.

It turned over once or twice and lay still. Along the path strode a man dressed in black: black gloves, black hat, and black walking-stick. Without pausing he put the end of the stick through the ring, lifted it, and walked on.

St William of Carileph came through the metal grille, bounded past Jude and Ange, and followed along the cathedral wall.

The weasel was saying, 'I knew I couldn't trust you, but I had to let you carry it. You've thrown away what I was in charge of.' It was beside Jude's clothes, springily on its toes, alert, eager to put matters right but not knowing how.

'It coughed itself out,' said Ange carefully, in case her whole self fell inside out from her mouth.

The weasel opened its jaws and chittered with great anger, partly at Ange, partly at the figure on the path. The rattling of its jaws turned into a scolding from Jude, a gush of bellowed words, ranting, screaming, furious.

The black figure swung the walking-stick. The golden ring at its end spun high into the air. He put out what should have been a hand to catch it. The hand was without flesh, only twigs of bone turning their hollow palm upwards.

St William had no worries about walking bones. He mounted a ledge, then sprang up into an archway higher again. The ring stood a moment level with him at the top of its flight. Sunset shot a beam through it to print its shadow on the wall. St William jumped. His paws closed on the ring.

Cats are more used to catching soft prey that a claw will grip. This cat fought to hold what he had caught, grappled what he could hardly feel, making random kicks and swipes, not having time to care which way up he would land.

He fell on to the black walking figure. It collapsed to the ground under him in a flutter of rags. The ring rolled on the path and lay there.

From the cloth on the path an activity rose, about the size of a terrier, but legged like a hunting spider, running for the bushes, then sidelong down the slope, helter-skelter under the trees, St William of Carileph close after him.

Ange saw Jude moving down from the cathedral wall, on all fours, perhaps a weasel still, perhaps not, naked as a needle and as sharp, claws and teeth ready. She was down on the path as cat and creature careered through the undergrowth below. She had the ring in her hand. Then she was striding back up the bank, swearing at nettles on her skinniness.

There was a spitting and a rattling further down, where a fight took place. It ended with a great curse from St William, and Ange thought she saw a broken umbrella swimming in the river beyond.

St William came up the bank in an absurd kittenish way, bouncing on all fours, his tail twitching, and screeched again, triumphant. His enraged fur was fluffed out and ridiculous. He was more sinner than saint. He had won. He licked his chest, left side, right side, crossing himself.

'If it had been boys' clothes I would have put them on,' Jude was saying, now dressed, on the bank beside the cathedral. 'I was a boy weasel, a hob. I looked.'

Julian Westow came up the path, with his music case. 'What are you doing', he demanded, 'with our church cat and rubbish all over the place?'

143

St William of Carileph smiled from a distance, and went off alone to his evening prayers.

'We've been inside for something,' said Jude.

'I've got to go,' said Julian, himself and his voice fading slowly. 'Time to be going,' Mum was saying. 'You've had a long play.'

They were beside Chapel Stack, where the ground was like the bank beside the cathedral. It was no longer sunset, but towards the end of a dull afternoon. No warmth spread from this dark rock.

'What went down to the stream?' Mum was saying. 'I don't think I've seen anything like it. It worried me. We'll eat our biscuits and then go home. That would be best.'

'Yes,' said Ange, firmly. 'It would.' She went to sit near Mum.

'You haven't been fighting, have you?' asked Mum. 'I thought you were singing hymns.'

Jude made herself uncomfortable on a lumpy stone. 'We had to slip away for a moment,' she said. 'We weren't long.'

'Anything interesting?' said Mum, expecting Jude to begin one of her fancies.

'I haven't had time to look,' said Jude. 'Excuse me.' She opened a hand layered with dust, and showed the ring. 'It's ours,' she said.

Mum picked it up. The stone was red, the metal gold, marked with scratches on the outside, the inside smoothed by Cuddy's finger. It was small in Mum's hand.

'Don't put it on,' said Jude.

'Of course not,' said Mum, like Ange, not wanting to wear Fitch belongings next to her skin. 'Take it home before your mother misses it. It's valuable, and you shouldn't have brought it out here.'

'Animals don't know that,' said Jude.

'If you say so,' said Mum, unable to imagine what Jude meant. 'What about a biscuit?'

All Ange could taste was a black beetle that she had eaten; and tallow candle clogged her teeth.

'I could of eaten Ange,' said Jude, spraying crumbs. 'But I didn't. I was a polecat, very rare. She was a rat.'

'Mouse,' said Ange, but no one believed her.

'A *weasel* made a nest in the coffin,' said Elfrida. 'St William had to get rid of it. Weasels are *vermin*, you know.'

Rattle, *rattle*, rattle, went the beads.

Chapter Fourteen

'THERE'S a tinsel in this pie,' said Dad. 'The smoky golden sort.' He was poking about with a spoon and a fork and his fingers. 'I could get tinsellitis. When did you make it?'

'Plum and apple from the Show,' said Mum. 'If it's the First prize winner it's Mrs Obley's. If it's Second Ruth entered it, and the Third is a Miss Norris. The judges cut exhibits in half, and they are auctioned afterwards. I bought them and froze them down.'

Ange had been wondering about a hand in the undercrust of her helping, a diminutive drawing from a fine pen.

'You might have dropped one half,' said Dad. 'The other half will be fine.'

'Nonsense,' said Mum. 'They had good stout bottoms, grease-proof paper thick as cardboard. That was never cut in two and it's still here.

Ange ate her hand. It chewed up perfectly well. She had a Beowulfish gurgle deep inside.

Dad knifed the pie on to a plate and pulled out the wrinkled circle it had been cooked on. Sleeping apple slices shrugged their shoulders under a pastry quilt.

'Good God,' he said, 'what have we eaten? Some pigments are poisonous, arsenic and mercury, red lead. Have you any idea what this is?'

'I think you are making a fuss,' said Mum. 'It's a perfectly healthy pie.'

'I know what I'm talking about,' said Dad. 'This isn't

cardboard or grease-proof, but parchment from an illuminated manuscript written in seventh-century uncial script, an initial letter, probably from one of the Gospels. Why is Margaret Obley baking pies on our national inheritance?'

Mum knew what was important. She went out of the room and the telephone dial made scratching sounds as the number dug its way to its destination. Giving her a ring, thought Ange, going round the table and stacking up plates. You always get someone making that noise.

'Margaret,' Mum was saying. 'I bought three prize pies from the show, yours, and Ruth's and one from Keld House. We've been eating one, yes, the freezer, no, nothing wrong, but what did you put under them, you and Ruth, to keep them off the enamel? Because . . . yes, I would too . . . but Daniel . . . oh, that parchment, yes, I see. Daniel said parchment, yes, a circle. No, of course not, it was a good pie. Thank you.'

'So it was her,' said Dad. 'I'd have thought she was more enlightened than that.'

'It wasn't her,' said Mum. 'Or Ruth. She said parchment, but she means baking parchment, you buy it in the shops, a sort of paper. They didn't use any real parchment.'

'Then it's the Norrises,' said Dad. 'Why would they use something so valuable for cooking?'

He was in his study after that with a box of tissues and a saucer of water, dabbing and wiping, dipping and swabbing, Mum showing him cooking parchment in circles and strips.

He finished one side of his circle and laid it on a clean tissue. Ange brought another saucer.

'Some poor soul,' he was saying, 'sat in a cold cloister on a bleak hillside, on a day between the Roman civilization and the onset of the Middle Ages, and did those gilded letters, that drawing, that painting, ten or twenty thousand little red dots to the inch. He didn't get paid, he got up at two in the morning and went to bed when he fell over asleep. And some vandal uses it to bake a pie. Look, there is writing on the back, too. This is cathedral library stuff, before printed books. It's in Latin, with Anglo-Saxon words written in later underneath.'

Ange looked. The small scribbles under the larger writing were just what Jude used as make-up writing.

'Not the Gospels,' said Dad. 'But Biblical, all the same, look, *dixit Isaac patri suo: Pater me. At ille respondit: Quid vis, fili? Ecce, inquit, ignis et ligna; ubi est victima holoca* . . . It goes off the edge there in the middle of a word; but it's written in Anglo-Saxon underneath, *Fæder min ic ascie hwær seo offrung sie; her is wudu and fyr.* It's little Isaac asking Abraham who is going to be sacrificed, a sick joke because it was Isaac himself. We'll let that dry, and I'll go to Ancren Dale now – those Norris ladies have got to be stopped.'

Mum thought Dad was being illogical and old-fashioned. 'Better in daylight,' she said. He was mostly being Dad.

'Better still,' he said, 'if I wrote from the university. That brother of theirs? Could he do anything? This is going to cause a stir, so I'll say nothing about it for the time being.'

Ange went to bed. Beowulf had to go down to see the parchment, and then was happy to go to sleep.

'Nothing will happen tonight,' said Dad. 'Unless we get Old Testament colic, very painful.'

He knows everything, thought Ange, not believing but feeling a pain. Beowulf understood, she knew.

The next morning Ange met Ruth in the shop.

'What was it?' asked Ruth. 'Mother couldn't understand it at all. What had happened?'

Jude came in with a lot of money for sweets, fingering jelly babies, bright worms, and thin glossy liquorice, assembling her captives in a bag.

'The pie bottom had writing on it,' said Ange. 'And hands. It was a page of Bible.'

Jude chose a scarlet serpent.

'Who would do that?' said Ruth.

'Terrible stuff,' said Ange, 'about someone sacrificing his own son.'

'We're always doing that bit,' said Jude. 'We wanted to do it f'real with Freddy Wyvill, but Sister Gabriel—' She shook her head.

'We would never use the Bible instead of cooking parchment for a pie bottom,' said Ruth.

'It was one of the ladies at Keld House,' said Ange. 'Dad was furious. He thought he was eating tinsel, so he's going to write to them and get the rest of the circles.'

'He could just go,' said Jude. 'The circles are in the kitchen. They use them for anything. They stick them on broken windows, or to stand the teapot on. They'll want your piece back, not you having theirs.'

Ruth took her shopping and went home, her mother not quite pleased about pie bottoms. Ange tucked a bag of flour under her arm, sorry to feel that Ruth was not pleased with Mum either.

Jude stuffed her bag of sweets into a pocket, and a puff of icing sugar frosted her jeans. 'I'll come up with you,' she said, licking the end of a jelly fish, sucking it in and blinking with delight. 'And go to the ladies after dinner and take it back. They'll want it.' To clinch the deal she gave Ange a longish bite of bootlace.

'I can hear that bell,' she said, when they were only halfway to the house.

'It'll be something else,' said Ange, sure that Jude was

romancing. 'A train making the railway line buzz. They do. That's all.' Jude was absolutely not noticing she was not wanted, as well as being fanciful.

'I'll give you all my sweets,' said Jude, pulling the bag from her pocket. 'Then you'll know it's true.'

'I can't hear it,' said Ange. 'And it's mine, so I should; and you can *keep* your sweets, and don't come back with me.'

They had a quarrel, and a spitty fight. Usually Jude could manage on her own, but this time Ange joined in. She lost, crying out of anger and exasperation, Jude stinging with every word and kicking her on the legs. The sweets fell beside the wall, Ange could not see where she was going, and Jude did not care.

Mum came out to see what the fuss was about. Nobody knew, as usual. Instead of rescuing her own Ange she took hold of Jude and held her away. Before anyone could speak Ange had walked straight past, sure that nobody cared, dumped flour on the kitchen table, and gone up to her bedroom. Jude went out of the gate, picked up the sweets, because she never forgot anything, and came back into the garden to answer the bell.

'Jealous,' said Elfrida. 'I know what that *means*.'

'Don't bother,' said Beowulf. 'You just happen to be living here, and squatters don't have rights in my lair.'

'It isn't ringing,' Ange shouted from the window. 'Go away.'

'Just go out and tell her,' Mum said from downstairs.

'She is horrible,' said Ange.

'It's catching,' said Mum. 'But don't vex me.'

Jude picked her way between the fossils defiantly, like a guilty weasel, and took the bell from its place.

'That settles it,' said Ange, down the stairs to Mum. 'She's got to go. She's pretending.'

'I've seen *you* pretending to hear things,' said Mum, 'so why not let her have her fancies.'

'But I believe her,' said Ange. That it was true began to come over her like an actual tide, little waves at first, then surges to the shoulders, and then crests breaking over her head.

She was with Cuddy again, and he had been in the sea, praying. 'What can you hear?' she asked Jude.

'I heard the bell,' said Jude. 'He was in the water all night. Even if I close my eyes I might see him change his clothes. Oh, look, look. I want to be one of those.'

Cuddy was talking softly to animals Ange could not see. 'What are they?' she asked Jude.

'Not dogs or cats,' said Jude. 'Ask him.'

He won't hear, Ange thought. It's not me he wanted, but Jude. 'I can't see,' she said. 'I wish I could.'

'Otters,' he said, as if he were in the garden with them.

'They're drying him,' said Jude. 'They're breathing on him with hot breath.'

A tide mark of broken black weed formed on the grass of the garden, dry sand above, and sleek wetness below left by the ebbing tide. Waves washed across the garden gate, and Mum inside the house would be waist deep making buns.

Cuddy stood on the dry sand, while two otters pawed at him, sniffed at him, and drew the wet sea from his long cloak. While Mum was still creaming the butter and sugar, the otters went into the sea to play in overcurling waves.

Cuddy looked at them. He became quite real. The sea and sand went away. Mum, out of the water now, broke an egg into the bowl and added a spoonful of flour.

'We have been together,' said Cuddy, 'for more years than you can know. You have reclaimed six of the things I need for my journey.'

'He's wearing slippers,' Jude whispered to Ange.

'I can see him,' said Ange. 'Can you hear?'

'Watch,' said Cuddy, 'pray, in your own ways.'

Ange found herself leaning over and nipping Jude on the shoulder. Jude raised herself on hind legs to pounce on Ange. Cuddy knelt and parted them with his bare hands. A finger crossed Ange's open mouth, and her teeth caught it. She did not bite.

Jude was herself again, sitting on a stone in the garden, having listened, watched, and prayed for as long as it takes an otter to do those things.

'There is one more thing,' said Cuddy. 'One thing more will take me to Neorxenawang.'

'More otters,' said Jude. 'We will get them all.'

'There are many otters,' said Cuddy. 'I need not stay wet. But I cannot swim to the island. I could walk there dryshod if I went the way of the Northman's gods, over the rainbow. I do not believe that is the way. To find my way I must have the seventh thing. It is my leather wallet, where I keep a little bread for the Mass, alongside the word of God. When all these things are put together again I shall be ready to travel home. Where they are I shall be.'

He went away to duties in his own time. Ange understood, but Jude was hurt by being left, and blamed Ange. But neither of them wanted to quarrel again, since being otters.

They put the bell back in its hole, and went to the house. The cakes were sitting happy and yellow in the oven light, now and then having volcanic eruptions that left a scar on the top.

Mum brought out a cake, listened to it, and put it back for two minutes more. 'You can lick the bowl,' she said.

'We've got a mixer,' said Jude. 'But my Mum hardly ever

bakes, and I do like good clean cake.'

Mum wiped Jude's face afterwards. She tipped the cakes on to a rack. 'You can peel the paper off the bottoms,' she said. 'Carefully, because it's still hot.'

The circles came off with cooked crumb on them.

'Parchment,' said Ange, remembering other circles, examining these for tinsel and tiny hands.

'Oh, Jude,' said Mum, 'don't make a mess.'

'I'm folding it to get to the middle,' said Jude. 'I haven't got all the front teeth in the world just now. Look, you could put things in.'

'It's a wallet,' said Ange, not really thinking anything of the sort, but the words came ready with the thought.

'Oh,' said Jude, 'I see, I see.' She took another double tongueful of crumbs from her wallet of grease-proof.

'What do you see?' asked Mum, lifting the last things out of the sink and stacking them to dry. 'Get out of it, you.' She was talking to eggshells, which had jumped in the water as she pulled out the plug to empty the sink.

'Just one of those things,' said Jude. 'These things. I can get them. There's all sorts of bits in there. She keeps them in the kitchen, but she doesn't say. I won't go near the experiment room. That isn't where they cook cakes.'

Ange thought that pie bottoms might be made of leather, and so might wallets, but it didn't mean that all pie bottoms were bound to be wallets.

They went out to look for the tide on the grass.

'Is he still about?' said Jude. 'He isn't listening.'

'Don't do anything changeable,' said Ange. 'I don't really like it very much.'

'I don't mind what else I am,' said Jude. 'I was born to be different. I want to tell him that I knew what he wanted all the time, if it's just old leather.'

Her father's empty wagon went booming by. She ran off home at this signal for tea. 'If there isn't any I'll be back,' she said.

Mum was lining up red jam for the sponge. 'I thought we weren't going to talk about pieces of leather,' she said.

'I didn't,' said Ange. 'Ruth asked me why you rang her mother, so I told her. Jude heard. She's not thinking about writing at all. Just now I knew why she was wrong, but when I think of it again she's right.'

'She'll forget,' said Mum.

Jude came up on Saturday at ten o'clock, dragging a full plastic carrier, a very dirty woollen shawl tucked on top of the contents.

'I got it,' she said. 'My Mum was up there cleaning today. She has so much work there no wonder she can't do her own house as well, she says.'

Ange was having breakfast alone. Mum had had hers, and Dad was pottering about upstairs, shaving and dressing. Mum washed Jude's face at the sink, combed her hair, and sat her at the table.

'You haven't eaten anything yet,' she said. 'And you can't sit here and watch other people.'

Jude smiled and enjoyed the fuss. 'I like being at a table,' she said. 'They do it all the time at Keld House.'

Dad looked at the used table, decided against breakfast, and went into his study to read.

'I'll take him some coffee soon,' said Mum.

Ange's room would do for an office, Jude said. There she spread the grubby shawl on the bed and tipped out the contents of the carrier. 'It's everything there was. I just told Miss V

I wanted them, and she took me there. She doesn't always know where the chocolate is, because the others hide it in different places, but she knows where she cuts pie bottoms.'

The heap was not so much pie bottoms themselves as pages with circles already cut out of them, where a pie bottom had been taken. Three or four were untouched, still stitched together in a little booklet with a flat thread, and nothing written in it. The parchment was rigid with age and bowed with living in a drawer among other kitchen things.

The cut sheets had wriggles of black words round the holes, as if caterpillars had eaten circles.

'See,' said Jude, finding a metal disk. 'She uses this for a pattern. The scissors are tied to the dresser in case she loses them. When the ladies bake she cuts the bottoms.'

'My Dad should see these,' said Ange. 'It's history, you know.'

'She gave them to me,' said Jude. 'There's enough here to make a wallet for his credit cards, to use on his holiday island. That's religion. He'll have a beach umbrella. But he'll look funny bathing in that cloak he wears.'

'Can Dad have one piece?' said Ange. 'To match the bit he's got.'

Jude agreed to that. Ange went down to the study and took the coffee in. She knew what she wanted. She asked to borrow the pie bottom for a minute or two, but it was at the University.

'You can have a photograph,' Dad said. 'Why?'

Ange smiled and took the photograph and found the hole it had left. 'He'll like that,' she told Jude.

'I'm going now,' said Jude. 'I'm taking it all but that. We've done all this stuff for Cuddy, and this is the last thing. I'm off to Edward, and it's going in the box. No one will stop me, because I know it's right. But,' she added, digging in her pocket, 'you look after this because it's like haunting our house.' She held out

155

a black-lined palm with the golden ring on it, the red stone seeking Ange's eye. 'Take it,' she said.

With that she packed the parchment up again, old and scentless, brittle but still slightly pliable, and prepared to go home. She went downstairs in a business-like way, thanked Mum for breakfast, and went off down the road.

'What a funny little thing,' said Mum. 'But why am I worrying? I've got you.'

Ange went upstairs slowly and put the warm ring at the back of her hankies, resting on a lace one.

Beowulf had a strip of parchment ruff called *on assum ridende* at one end, and *stravit asinum* at the other.

'No, I don't know,' he said. 'Is it a compliment to me?'

'Probably,' said Elfrida. 'It means, riding on a *donkey*.'

Beowulf said no more. He saw a shameful picture of himself balanced on two wheels, now that meat donkeys were forgotten.

Chapter Fifteen

'Jude brought it this morning,' said Ange, wishing Dad would sit down calmly and eat his food. 'She had a bundle of it and she's taken it away.'

'My own house filled with manuscripts from the Dark Ages,' said Dad. 'I'm in the house and no one tells me, I don't get a look. It's a sad state of affairs when anybody, just anybody, can take our priceless heritage and, and, and, bake it to death, and give the remains to a barbarian child to do what she likes with. And you knew,' he said to Ange, reproachfully, not cross, but disappointed with her and Jude, and Keld House. 'You borrowed the photograph and got the rest of the page. But if there are hundreds of other pages I should be told.'

'She'll keep them carefully,' said Ange. 'For now.' But she knew they would be in a different keeping soon.

'They don't bake at Jude's house,' said Mum, giving Dad more coffee. 'It's all frozen or tins. They won't get cooked.'

Dad sat down, fingering the strip of parchment with *asinum* on it, getting food halfway to his mouth and then thinking of something to say and not saying it. 'That grimepot, Jude,' he said at last, making faces because the cabbage was cold, still back in the Dark Ages of the meal.

Ange sat in her room, feeling guilty though she was not at fault. She took out the ring, and wiped Jude's pocket stickiness from it.

She remembered a tuft of hair from a certain tree, and began to tease that into a thread, about as long as from elbow to wrist, twisting it and pulling it together.

She threaded it through the ring, and began to tie a thumb knot to hold it safe. At that moment Beowulf somersaulted from the top of the dressing table, knocking ornaments and pot creatures to the floor, jumped across to the bed, hit Ange sharply in the face, and—

'What is it?' said Mum, coming up the stairs at the noise of little statues skittling about.

'I'm just sitting here,' said Ange, startled, frightened, but feeling very safe with Beowulf. Beowulf, in addition to hurtling across the room, had stamped her new thread to pieces, and then collapsed like any stuffed toy.

Mum put the mirror upright again. 'The wind,' she said, closing the window, drawing a curtain. Ange put the ring away again, picked up the scattered hairs of the thread, laid them on the dressing table, and went down to the fireside.

Beowulf was pleased with himself. 'I flew like a bee.'

'You suffer from *pride*,' said Elfrida. 'Even if you acted rightly – you should ignore heathen *magic*.'

'Wolf hair through a golden ring,' said Beowulf. 'She did not know, but it was a very bad spell.'

'*Nothing* to be excited about,' said Elfrida. 'Only your *duty*. I shall pray for *you* calmly.'

The next morning was Sunday. Mum went to church early and then cooked breakfast.

'Julian Westow has this weekend off,' she said. 'He and Robin are going to see Edward. I met them in the street. It must be Edward's birthday, but I don't think much of the presents, an old stick, and a sort of rotted comb and strange scissors. I thought it was all high-tech these days.'

It was high-tech then, thought Ange. They must take a million hours to make with a penknife. And getting the right stick needs stuff like miracles. And then she was glad she had these thoughts and memories to measure life against.

'It'll be a game,' Mum decided. 'With treasures and levels and all-time high scores and so on, virtual reality, making life more like a computer.'

'That's like what I was thinking,' said Ange. 'Only the opposite as well.'

Not long afterwards the telephone rang. Ruth wanted Ange to go over that afternoon, 'bringing something,' she said.

'Bringing what?' asked Mum.

'Oh,' said Ange, knowing very well what Ruth meant, 'it'll be a party for Beowulf. A picnic. He'll like that.'

Beowulf went down with her for the event, in the cloth bag from Cyprus. Under him was the bell, the true thing that had to be taken, its open mouth silent except for a calm tide running on a smooth shore, and a wind gathering lumpy on the horizon. In Ange's pocket was the ring, the other true thing, bright, cold, and safe.

Ruth met her in the village. 'We're going to Edward's,' she said. 'But we won't do it there. We'll have to go up into Ancren Dale.'

'Hopeless here,' said Edward, in the yard of the Swan Inn. 'They think it's every toy there ever was, and I can't keep them away.' The bullet-headed twins were clambering in and out of the oak box, knowing it was their tractor.

Edward was trying to wrest the tool called a fore-hammer from them before they smashed the lid with it. 'If it'll break things, it belongs to the Smiths,' he said patiently, putting the hammer out of reach and being bitten by both.

Jude shouted at them fiercely for shaking the wood when she was trying to draw on it. 'It's hard enough to remember what a polecat saw,' she said. 'And now they're getting at my bag of wallets. Can't you fasten them up, Edward? Them brats.'

Until he did Jude idled about, gathering wood shavings and putting them in her hair, catching one of Edward's family pigeons and, it seemed to Ange, painting its claws black.

'I'm sending a postcard,' said Jude, 'that's all.' She held up a wood shaving speckled with marks from her brush, snipped off a bight of her own hair with Edward's shears, and wound the hair into a ring. The pigeon flew to the letting-board of the cree, and then into the sky. Jude gave the brush to a twin to lick.

'Is that the message I got a long time ago?' said Ange. She had seen the wood shaving long before it was made. 'Sitting on the doorstep?'

Jude's face wrinkled up into happy belief. 'I remember,' she said, as if nothing else could ever have been possible. 'Well?' she asked. 'Did you bring that other thing you're looking after?'

The clean ring went back into a sticky pocket. Jude got her brush again and began to draw on the box.

Julian and Robin played with the twins for an hour before Jude had finished the decorating, remembering what she had seen of Cuddy's box under the cathedral floor, when the light came through the trapdoor. 'I've done all I saw,' she said. She had used up all the black paint.

'I think they're people,' said Ange. 'That bit's upside down.' There had been things like it in Cyprus.

'I looked from the top,' said the polecat, blacking her fingernails with the last dregs of paint. 'And it was dark most of the time.'

The twins were abandoned behind their gate. Edward put the electric screwdriver in the box. He took a handle at one corner,

160

Robin another, Julian the third, and Ruth the fourth.

'You two girls carry what goes in it,' Ruth said.

There was no one in Ancren Dale. Over in the direction of the Hall three ladies, their brother and his dog, walked off the skyline out of sight.

'What do we do first?' asked Julian. He expected some known thing to happen, since the others had done it more often. 'Nobody's told me the game.'

'We don't know,' said Robin. 'We never did it before. It does it, or it doesn't. These things go in the box, and the lid goes on, and that's all we know. We don't even know that, but we can't think of anything else.'

'Is that it?' said Julian. 'A bit ordinary?'

The others walked on, hoping things might remain a bit ordinary. Ange found her heart beating quick and firm as they came up the path. In Ancren Dale, she still sensed her own blood at her fingertips.

'Here,' said Edward, beyond Chapel Stack, and beside the water. 'In the middle of this place.'

'Where *I* saw him *first*,' said Jude. 'Of course.'

They put the box on the grass. Edward twirled out with his fingers two screws that held the lid in place. Inside the box were half a dozen more screws and the screwdriver. He lifted them out.

'We'll put the things in,' he said solemnly, 'fasten the lid on, and go away.'

'For ever,' said Jude. 'He'll leave on his holiday then. It's for the rest of his life, but I think it's for the rest of his not-life, because he knows he's dead even if he thinks he isn't.'

'We got the bell first,' said Ange. 'At the top of the waterfall. Shall I just stand it in?'

161

It seemed too humble an action to have a meaning, and no meaning appeared. Ange stood it in the box, with a dedication in her mind but unspoken; and it was silent, one thing out of seven. 'Not an imitation,' she said. 'That bell called his people to prayer. I was there.'

'I'll just put the stick in,' said Robin. 'Sort of cornerwise. I was there too.'

The second object went in. 'We're putting him together,' said Ruth. She had the parts of the third object, the patterned morse with its lengths of chain, and the gold thread from the bratt, hard and scoury, like a kitchen scrubber. She had rubbed the morse bright. She had rinsed the thread and tried to make it neat as well, but the pattern was in a braided tangle. 'I hope he does not mind,' she said, spreading the gold out as wide as she could. 'It is meant to be a garment.'

'It doesn't look like anything or anybody,' said Jude. 'Are we doing something daft? Will he mind?'

'We just can't understand,' said Julian. He had his contribution in a box, and brought it out. 'I dusted them,' he said. 'That's all. If he used them there might be his own hair in them; you know how it gets into a comb.'

'Yes,' said Ange, recalling great cotters, tangles that had to be dragged out. 'You get split ends.'

'I'll put them down by his feet,' said Julian. 'He can easily get them up.' He laid the fragile remains against the end of the box.

Ange looked round. Nothing is happening, she thought. We are doing it wrong. Robin stood aside. He had to be guided by Ruth.

Edward had the cup in a pocket. 'We can't have wine,' he said, 'but we can get water from the stream.' He dipped it from a flowing place, and put the cup where a hand might be if Cuddy were in the box.

Ruth looked at Jude. 'You've got two things,' she said.

'One,' said Jude. 'I got the ring.' It was deep in her pocket, full of fluff again. She had to blow the fluff away. She gave the ring a polish on her leg, and held the sombre stone out. It was not seeking eyes today.

'In here,' she said. 'His right hand is here.' She laid the ring where she thought proper. She stepped back. 'I want to go in there too,' she said. 'It's perfect where he's going, but you can't go for a fortnight, only for ever.'

'Yes,' said Ruth, not briskly, exactly, but not allowing any gaps in what went on. 'What about the bag of stuff?'

'It'll be from everyone,' said Robin. 'There should be seven of us for seven things, but only six came.'

Jude held out the bag, for once wanting to do things in the most proper way. 'It's from Keld House. They're the seventh lot, on a different side and don't know.'

'We'll each put some in for them,' said Ruth gently. 'I hope it's a wallet. My Granda takes his bait in one, a bag he wraps round things.'

This is not magic enough, Ange was thinking. This is not what the postcard said. But it never is so sunny if you visit the place. She took her share of pie-bottom pages, and laid them down with the rest. A breeze rattled the sturdy sheets.

'Now the lid,' said Edward, lifting it and placing it. He dropped a screw into a hole at one corner, the same at the diagonal, and a third in another hole. The rest he laid on the lid for the others to place and begin to fit.

He went round tightening the screws with the electric screwdriver. 'Fully charged,' he said.

He meant the screwdriver, but Ange felt that something else was charged as well. They had assembled seven things, and made more than a heap of objects. They created another quality.

'It was all rubbish, you know,' said Robin, feeling the same thoughts. 'Until he did it.'

The screwdriver went into the plastic bag when the job was done. Edward said. 'Now what do we do? Just go home?'

'We don't know any more,' said Ange. She remembered telling Dad that she would bring him the parchment one day, and now she had helped leave it out of reach for ever. And even Beowulf, in his cloth bag, seemed a little blurred with tears of farewell and disappointment.

There was silence in Ancren Dale for the space of half an hour.

'I smell the sea,' Cuddy said. 'Birds are singing on the waves.' The wind sighed and brought briny richness with it. 'I shall be able to cross it to the island, Neorxenawang, Paradise.'

'Have we done it right?' asked Edward.

'I hope I shall do as well in my turn,' said Cuddy. 'That test comes soon. I believe that I am right and shall conquer. But fighting myself is the hardest fight of all.'

'It's worse for me too,' said Jude, sympathetically.

Elfrida had something to say but for once remained silent. Beowulf understood her perfectly.

'I've been watching so far,' he said. 'Now I have a deed to do. Cuddy put on his cloak and his ring, picked up his stick, rang his bell and sent me away. I was frightened. People have no teeth to speak of, no claws, and I'm four times their size. But it was atelic. I ran away, ashamed.'

'So you *should* be,' Elfrida almost said.

'I came back because he wanted me,' Beowulf continued. 'I was his guard, his heavy. I caught fish for him. Now there is

164

something I wish not to do. I am plain scared of it, I don't know what it is, I don't want to do it, and I have to.'

Elfrida prayed, busy among beads, lips jogging out words desperately. 'I try to *help*,' she said, between Amens.

Cuddy said, 'I am waiting for seven. Who else is coming?'

Beowulf, Ange thought. The electric screwdriver.

'How should we know anyone else?' asked Ruth.

'Seven of you,' said Cuddy, 'took me from Lindisfarne and the fury of the Northman, to a hundred years of safety.'

He looked up the valley side at a pillar of stone like a solitary gatepost, furred green with age. There were straggling but unknown letters on it, and a cross, carved under lichen. Beside it water ran from the ground into a stone basin, overflowing in a silver curtain. 'Water is a blessing,' he said, dipping his fingers in and touching each of their heads with it.

He was not a big man. Julian was heavier, Robin shorter, but with wider shoulders. Edward would always be skinnier. Ruth, as tall herself, gave him a curtsey. Ange tried the same thing, but stumbled on a tussock of grass.

To Jude he said, 'Are you the seventh one? Something about you speaks of other things.'

'I don't know,' said Jude. 'Can I hold your hand?'

'I hold all your hands,' said Cuddy. 'I am your burden.'

'What *are* you talking about?' said Jude, taking him over. 'I know what it's like, having no friends.'

'When the Northman came to these shores in greed, he first of all attacked Lindisfarne,' said Cuddy. 'But he had come, almost in peace, many times before that, to all Northumbria, and to Dal Riada, and many other places. His keels came in spring, with ice on their land, when flowers were already here. He brought sleeping bees in skeps, and left them all summer,

165

coming before winter to take them away again, in big round baskets, dripping with honey. When he found Lindisfarne's gold tasted better than honey he chased the poor brothers out into the great dark, often for ever. They had no stings.'

'The ships were black,' said Edward.

'The heart was black,' said Cuddy. 'You know the rest, because you took me from Lindisfarne. You hid the seven parts of my life.'

For him there was nothing between the Northman, a very unpleasant set of persons, and now.

The sea was ahead and below, neither calm nor stormy, but uneasy, twitching its tail and showing it had claws.

'From the bell to bring people to prayer, to the wallet itself,' said Cuddy, 'you have each brought back one of those things, so that I am able to travel. This stone has a cross, one of the marks of life, its beginning and end. It is the wolf-hoofed-tree, the gallows, the cross of my faith.'

Ange understood what had happened on Merrylaw, what wolf-hoofed tree she had run against – but not yet what wolf.

'Holiday,' said Jude. 'I knew.'

'What did you know?' asked Cuddy. 'Who is the seventh who provided my wallet?'

'Miss Victoria,' said Jude. 'But she doesn't do anything on purpose, unless she's a witch.'

'She's a sort of cousin,' said Julian. 'They all are. People say so because they want to be related to a grand family.'

'We are all related to that,' said Cuddy. 'We work at it all our lives. A dead saint is not dead bones, but lives to bring his brothers and sisters closer to the grand family. It is time to go to my last, and first, grave. But I have to face the seventh person, who should be here and is not. Seven guardians took care of me while there was danger from the Northman, and were blessed and rewarded, and given land, so that they would always be ready.'

'Given land?' said Jude. 'You can't get given land. Where would you put it? Land is big. It has to stay where it is.'

'You put your house on some of it, Judith,' said Ruth. 'You farm it, you build walls round fields, and you put cows in the fields.'

Jude thought that was very foolish. 'Who wants cows', she said, 'slopping on the grass?'

Ange did not listen. She saw once more, not very far away, the otologist being a soldier. She glimpsed again the thing in the courtyard like the chicken-bone loom, wolves walking like trees, Mr Norris with the gun, the leader of the pagans at Merrylaw, the helicopter pilot, the black-clothed man by the cathedral; the brother of something like witches.

She saw them all coming clear on the grass against the sea. They seemed separate but were all one thing, with different aspects coming and going.

'Be of good cheer,' said Cuddy, who had waited to speak again. 'I have more to say. This is my ownself and my enemy, the seventh member of the company. There is always one who goes across to another side. We are all free to believe and allowed to be wrong. He is coming back now, and we are together after all the time since I was last alive.'

There were dragons, and flags, and the noises of flying and wind in the furls, scratching distant on all their ears, coming closer.

167

Chapter Sixteen

A LL of them stepped forward to meet what they saw and did
not wish to resist.

Ange saw dragons she longed to stroke and bring to hand.

'The helicopter again,' said Jude, not alarmed, though
excited by what she saw. 'Last time the windows twankle more.'

'Hope they've got some brakes,' said Robin, cheerfully.

Edward's eyes opened in a wide stare, and his lips parted. He
was rising into the air, leaving the ground.

'Music!' said Ruth, delighted, and happy. 'The music! We
can dance.'

Each saw a different thing. Jude babbled about a ride; Ruth
saw the music of an orchestra or band; Edward knew he could
now fly; Robin longed to drive one of them, and expected to.

Ange's dragons swept up into a star-burst, and swooped,
touching the ground with a claw.

'Sweet,' she thought and said. 'Like kittens.' She knew as
well that kittens scratch, and that the beautiful dance was more
dangerous than kittens.

'It's what I want,' said Ruth, trying to edge aside some other
person who stood in the way. Ange too tried to edge round the
nuisance. 'Excuse me,' said Jude to this other person.

'You must look,' said Cuddy, who was that other person.
'But this is not what you have come for. Do not see what is not
there. We all bring dreams into our world, but dreams cannot
be real.'

Robin said, 'It was one of the . . . no, a . . . it should have had wheels, not legs.'

Jude said, 'But I wanted it to kidnap me, and like me.'

'You see alien appearances,' said Cuddy, 'alien ships, strangers to our world. Take care, because they bring their own gods. There is only one God, and He is here already. I had to find that myself. So look at what you wished to love, and think again. Strange gods are beautiful. They tear at your heart. I tell my people so all the time, and they tell me. But that beauty is only seen; it is not truly there.'

Ange's flight of dragons resolved into a bitty cloud, coils of blackish brown dust, distant swirls drifting down the sky. A headache settled between her eyes, where she had been eaten by no dragons.

Edward still stared, his mouth tight, his feet light on the grass. 'I am,' he said. 'I am.'

What was approaching flickered in and out of its disguises.

Cuddy still spoke. 'I was a soldier, before I was a shepherd; iron sword, iron spear, iron armour. Now my weapon is reality, my armour truth and love.'

The difference is, Ange saw, that Cuddy is in colour, and the other thing is like a black and white fire. It is there, it is moving, but it is making the world crooked.

'Oh,' said Ruth, 'it is disgusting. It is not music at all. It is not even noise.' She opened her mouth in a wide slot and moved her jaws, getting rid of a foul taste.

Edward came to the ground, and staggered to get his footing. 'I was flying,' he said, 'until you made it look awful.'

'It is the Northman's war god, Tyr,' said Cuddy. 'The seventh guardian took the shape of Tyr. Tyr lost his right hand in the mouth of Fenris the wolf, breaking a promise. The wolf took it and is with him at all times. Tyr will fight with his left hand, and I shall fight with mine, because I am left-handed too, what they call cuddy-wifted. If he wins, then all I have done is worth nothing. But if I win, then so will he. Watch and pray for victory for both of us. We have watched and prayed before.'

'I think I had better come with you,' said Jude. 'I can do that sort of stuff. We're all left-handed too.'

'You do not know which side you are on,' said Cuddy. 'It is not what you think you want, but your nature, that leads you. I go alone.'

'Oh frig,' said Jude.

'Do not call upon strange gods,' said Cuddy.

'I am his bouncer,' said Beowulf, 'his heavy. So I must help. But what can I do? My left arm, my fighting arm, is a dead nun.'

'No,' said Elfrida. 'Oh no. It is a *living* nun! Alleluia!'

'I've been at battles before,' Beowulf muttered. 'That's Tuesday for you.' Tuesday is Tyr's day: Beowulf knew. He growled the song of warrior angels, in a voice deep again with time.

Cuddy went alone. Tyr walked with hollow tread to meet him, neither of them ready to give in.

The wolf stood back and snarled. A bear, quite distinct to be seen, heaved its way past Cuddy, held the wolf with its eye, and stood waiting. The wolf had lowered its head and its back bristled large at the sight of its enemy, Cuddy. It possibly thought that Beowulf was a small, worn, stuffed toy, until Beowulf laid a paw on it. The back hair of both of them bristled. Teeth glittered, sharp and yellow.

'We shall sit together,' said Ruth, gathering the others in front of her beside the tall stone, 'and hope he wins, because otherwise I don't know how to get us home again.'

A stone's throw away Cuddy and Tyr were face to face.

Cuddy was small and dressed in a habit or cloak not quite white, but clean.

Tyr had become himself. He was not something that dressed. He was black, because where he could be seen there was nothing there for ever; he was also white, like bone, as a shadow of the blackness, the horror of empty infinity discovered sometimes in nightmare or delirium.

He was also a warrior solid in muscle, long-haired, wild, red-eyed, lips drawn back, balanced on ready feet.

'He's got nothing on,' said Jude.

'It is your imagination,' said Ruth.

Cuddy put up a hand, and Tyr took it, closing a fist like a mailed gauntlet on it. He began to exert strength. Cuddy bowed with pain but did not submit at all.

One eye of Tyr bulged, the other grew smaller, and his mouth was distorted sideways. This was his beginning of strength, his mood of fight. This was the intimidation of the destroying warrior, the berserker, brought about by dedication and training.

The air tightened down all round, compressed and thin, cold as winter, in the stillness snow being squeezed from the icy tension.

Cuddy resisted. His shoulders hunched, and he sang something to hearten himself. He stood his ground. He pushed forward, and the battle was carried across the hillside.

Tyr pressed hard, the sinews of his neck and forehead growing taut. The foam of spittle stood about his lips. Ange heard his heart like the demented barking of a chained dog. His arms and joints shook like a tree in a storm, exerting the pressures of a hurricane, and every muscle protruded like a clenched human fist. This was his beginning of mad power.

It is like a cartoon, Ange thought, drawn too wild. Cuddy

laid his gentle hand on those angered limbs and held firm.

The earth dithered under them, heaved like a small sea, and rock knocked on rock, twitching and uneasy. Below it were shouts, the running of feet, and the dint of weapons. There was war below, as there was war above. Tanks grumbled and their tracks squealed; Ange smelt the dirty diesel in her throat; she saw smokes rising; a gun fired down in the layers of geology, among the dinosaurs.

More immediately, something tore at the turf, like sheep eating but more deadly, the point of a spear lifting through the grass, red and scratched, beside her feet. Somewhere beyond Jude the sod was split by the blade of an axe striking up from below. The brutal noise of these strokes shook the table of sea and land, and the helmet of sky on it juddered. The horizon split apart. There was darkness beyond.

In that battle men ran shouting, and something followed rattling like a hurrying skeleton. Restless ground subsided. Earth and sky throbbed like a headache.

Drops of blood gathered at the roots of Tyr's hairs, and sucked them into his scalp; he turned and turned where he stood, and his chest expanded until there were gaps between his ribs that a man's fist might enter. This was his store of might.

Lightning danced overhead, and thunder rippled. Winter clamoured above the sky. The fight began to use the clouds, drawing them over that one place.

The wolf howled. The bear, on all fours, leaned towards it, laying the pressure of size against it. Neither looked away from the other. This was a second battle, wary and nervous.

Tyr began to screech, not with a voice but by making himself vibrate, trying to drown Cuddy's words. But Cuddy's words rode over the thunder, pulled startlingly out of that chest, marching and treading on Tyr's clamour.

172

'That's a God song,' said Jude. 'We have it at Mass.'

Now Tyr was walking through Cuddy, treading him down, to overcome him by weight. His feet, like iron stumps, pressed on Cuddy's leather slippers, his legs overbearing Cuddy's. This was his world, his charge of history, and his great will. He seemed sure to overpower, to crush, to destroy. Mere cloud overhead gave way to sky lit with curtains of swinging light, the aurora, the rainbow bridge of Bifrost, descending to lead Cuddy captive along the road of the Northman's gods.

'He's losing,' said Robin. 'We should help.'

'We'll do as he asked,' said Ruth. 'Wait. Sit down.'

Robin sat down, Ruth having the right answer once again, because there was nothing they might do.

In the other confrontation the bear made his first stroke with a great left claw. The wolf drew back its head and showed a range of teeth, white as mountains. The bear cuffed it again. The wolf howled; the bear crackled with fury.

Cuddy continued to sing. The fight was no longer moving about, and stood in one place. The battle dissolved without losing its taut presence. There was now none of the flinging about of real wrestling; there were no blows struck by boxers; there was no clash of weapons. There was only Cuddy letting the darkness of infinity fill his own person, drawing it into him; being consumed by Tyr.

But it seemed that Tyr was not overwhelming Cuddy. Cuddy's voice either sounded firmer, or Tyr's had grown less loud, less insistent. They were standing on the same ground. First the feet belonged to both, and they both stood on the same legs; and, as lightning sprang from Tyr's head, their bodies filled the same space; and then only Cuddy's arms were lifted up; and at last the fearsome black warhead of the Norse god was prayed out of existence, blotted out by Cuddy, absorbed and dried, withering out of sight.

The snow dried like powder; the earth rested, and the rafale of thunder turned to a retreat of war horns; that too turned to another music, marching away, and then advancing in a chorus of song, jubilant and joyful, celebrating the fight without showering disgrace on Tyr, welcoming him. When the music finished there was peace.

Cuddy knelt, and a very uncertain wolf watched from a distance, one paw held up pathetically, wanting to go but not being sure what it was leaving. It turned away and walked off, tail low, head low, looking back occasionally. Cuddy rang his bell, and the wolf turned, waved its tail and lifted its head.

Beside it, for a while, walked the bear, one hand comfortingly on its flank, as if the wolf were a pet. But they had not fought to a standstill, only for honour, and both gained that.

'We are wild beasts,' Beowulf was saying to the wolf. 'It is our nature to be wild, as it is the nature of water to be wet and cold.'

'There *is* nothing left *for* you to do,' said Elfrida.

'What is that?' asked the wolf. 'Rabies?'

'Indigestion,' said Beowulf. 'Something I ate. Goes on repeating. You be on your way. Our kinds don't quarrel. You are free, but I belong to one of them.'

'Like a cat,' said the wolf.

'Worse,' said Beowulf. 'I only have one life and it goes on all the time. But we've done our duty by them, and by one another, and I wish you rich hunting.'

A smiling lady came to meet her brother's dog. It licked her hand and began to follow her. Then it turned, picked something up from the heather, and, as a wolf again, brought it gently to

Ange. Ange put Beowulf in the bag.

Cuddy still knelt. His singing was done. Jude went to stand by him. He put a hand flat on the grass and heaved himself up. The salt of his sweat sparkled on his forehead.

He was smiling and happy. 'It's very simple,' he said. 'I do not take from people. I tell them there is much more than they realized. I told Tyr the same. He was all very well in his way, but being a god of war is a very limiting occupation, and not many are happy or satisfied. I have simply shown him that what I know about is bigger than all he knows. He was one room, which some people thought was a grand one, and there was certainly fire and feasting; but the house of God has rooms full of mansions, and you can go in and in and in, finding more and more, banquet after banquet. I have not taken anything from Tyr. I have shown him things greater than he knew. But Tyr was all the time in myself, and it is myself that I have fought against, and against myself the battle was decided. So that is done. He was the seventh guardian, in whatever form he took. Now I shall go to my island, but not across Bifrost. I have dealt at last with the Northman, the Norse, the Norris – all the same thing.'

In spite of his smile he now trod wearily. Jude wrapped his arm round her. Julian took his other side, and they helped him up the hill.

The crest of the hill was the top of a cliff. The sea licked among rocks below, and gulls rose on a lifting wind. Cuddy raised his voice.

'Neorxenawang,' he called. 'I have the means to reach it. But I need your help still. We must go down the cliff.'

Ange saw nothing but sea, and magnifications of it when the wind pulled tears from her eyes.

They went down the cliff with the gale holding them to it. The path was built for birds, pasted on a vertical face, thinned down to a thread between pinnacles. At its foot the sea paced among rocks and snarled in narrowing passages.

'We can't walk out in that,' said Ruth. Ange had a clear picture of Cuddy calmly stepping into the tide and walking all night, if necessary, through the water to get to his island.

'It is better than my island,' said Cuddy. 'Not just the best a man can do for himself and God, but Paradise. Do you see it?'

No one was sure that anything could be seen. The sea had a blue mist on it, and at the horizon could not be distinguished from sky.

'We shall get there,' said Cuddy. 'We have the boat. It is a simple one.' He took his leather wallet from his cloak and dropped it into the water. 'The writing on it might contain the whole world,' he said. 'It can withstand water, and hold us. It could hold ten thousand, if so many remain alive in the world today after the Northman has passed, or Doomsday. Has there been Doomsday?'

'Not in our district,' said Robin, very gravely.

'It is to come,' said Edward, at least sounding more exact.

'I don't know all the days,' said Jude. 'Some have names like Christmas, or yesterday, or my Mum's best day, never.'

'Tyr's day is Tuesday,' said Cuddy. 'He is not forgotten.' He calmly watched the wallet. It stayed where it was, bobbing on the inflow and outflow of water. It began to change, to unfold, to lengthen, to grow bigger. 'The shepherd's purse. It grows anywhere, if we look.'

The hard parchment softened into leaves, like slices of velvet liver in the gravy of the sea. It swelled and floated shapeless and dark.

The early pumpkin is turning into a coach, Ange thought. I am the mouse and the horses.

'Maybe we are getting smaller,' said Cuddy. 'Who can tell?

We do not know our size.'

'It's always happening,' said Jude, sure she should be growing a weasel tail and becoming a hob.

The wallet had opened out like a paper boat, with a frame inside. It floated in an inlet, rising and falling, ready and waiting.

'They are great boats for going to Ireland,' said Cuddy. 'But there have been accidents. Books of the Gospel have been lost, but since they are the world of life, life brings them back to the shore and stains them hardly at all. Shall we get in?'

'We could just see you off,' said Ruth, cautiously, not thinking the idea a very good one.

'You will come back,' said Cuddy. 'Look, seals are watching us.'

'And otters,' said Jude, all teeth and shivering smile.

'I shall get in first,' said Cuddy. 'To keep the vessel steady.'

Julian stepped off a rock after him. Robin followed, staying half in the boat, half on land, to help the rest in.

'Lie on the bottom,' said Cuddy. 'We shall be taken.'

They were suddenly in rainbows, and the surges of the sea were like music. They were riding the waves on a gentle road, slow up and slow down. Gulls were wheeling in a wide arch above them. Beside them the seals looked to Cuddy, and among them bobbed ducks, black against a sea green and transparent as glass, flecked with no more than a white foam. And smaller darker creatures smiled and mewed.

The island was ahead, shining on its own light, lying low in the water but perhaps having high hills inland, its shore empty and full of welcome.

Cuddy stood up. 'This joy is selfishness,' he said. 'Things should not be so simple.'

The boat ran up on land, the shingle rolling under it. A wave left it beached and still, and Cuddy stepped out.

'Neorxenawang,' he said. 'We are all here.'

There were times later on when Ange recalled scenes both fair and foul from the life of Cuddy.

There was the end of a long hungry day of rain, in an empty district between kingdoms. Towards sunset the rain had lifted, and a castle appeared, dark against the brightening sky. But when they toiled up the hill there was no castle. Only the bare rocks of nature lay wild and untouched, and no one to welcome them. They had thought of warmth and food, and it was hard to be without them.

'Let us pray that we do not mind,' Cuddy had said, 'that we accept what we cannot change; that nothing changes us.'

When they opened their eyes stone walls were round them, fire burning, meat roasting. Cuddy had laughed at their delight and served them with his own hands.

'It is always like this,' he had told them. 'There is more plenty than you need.'

Whether he had eaten for himself, or felt the fire, or slept on flat beds, none of them could tell. In the morning they woke refreshed but among rocks; no walls, no trace of hospitality, and where the fire had flamed, the turf healed whole again.

One day, like the day of the Glasgow Express, time was loose enough for Cuddy to see new animals, and to wonder at them.

'Rabbits,' Robin had said. 'Far too many of them.'

'The Northman brought the ginger cats,' said Cuddy, who had lived before them. 'And hares were always here. But what are these long-ears?'

Under the warm arches of a building that was part church, part hotel, the songs of the monks mingled with the baking of food. In the later afternoon sun the brothers pricked and made their parchments, gospelling out the words, laying the first capital letter out large as a page, surrounding it with leaping panthers, gazelles twisting their necks, dogs setting a hare or a boar. Sea birds curled like snakes in the margins, the clothes of the saints were like wedding garments.

Cuddy, this time in his box, filling the church with light at vespers, and the poor bringing their sick to be helped.

'God will provide,' said Cuddy. 'From outside, or within.'

They had looked to the sky, and an eagle rose up it towards them and let fall a salmon, close against the fire Cuddy had lit.

Not long afterwards a shy bear had led them to the nest of the bees, broken out a hanging rounded comb for them, and watched them bite the wax.

Cuddy had blown smoke to calm the bees. The bear sniffed it, knowing man only lit fire to calm bees or, in church, God.

Here too now was Tyr, walking free as if he were Mr Norris of Keld House. His right hand he had placed in the jaws of the wolf Fenris and then betrayed the wolf's trust. For that the wolf had closed its jaws, and Tyr gone without a right hand, left-handed but needing both. Those bones had been his presence many times, like a bundle of garden canes, rising as wings behind a stable block, a spider tempting in the castle in the forest, a dark stranger beside a cathedral, going like a cursor across that false screen. For Tyr the world was only a place for lost souls, until he found the many palaces within Cuddy.

The song of the boatmen, strange and wild, crossing the river, bearing their wood to the monastery. And years later monks not of the guild and without the skill trying the same thing. Cuddy on the bank, then in the water, working against the current, drawing the rafts into safety. There was a different song after that.

'If you understand there is a miracle,' said Cuddy, 'then there is.'

So it was on Neorxenawang itself, like a dream not resolved; the homeness of it, the festival, the satisfaction or fullness, the clear rightness of the place; and their mouths being filled though they did not eat, their hearts being content though they did not desire anything, their doubts banished, though they did not need to know anything.

How can having everything be enough, when wanting is the only way of measuring value?

Jude sat apart and took nothing, shaking her head when she was asked how she fared, and why she did not share the over-whelming plenty.

A minute later, or a year later, or somewhere out of time, Cuddy drew them together.

'You must go,' he said. 'What you have tasted is not a reward but another burden. You must return to your own places and people.'

'We are not ready for Paradise,' said Ruth, sensibly but sadly. 'They will want us back.'

'Some might,' said Jude, climbing last into the boat.

'I will push you off,' said Cuddy. 'You will go safe to land.'

After that Ange was not sure what happened, because Jude was climbing out again as the boat took to the waves, tipping it to one side just as the water held one end.

The whole island blinking out of sight so firmly that Ange

could still see it in her closed eyes. Without an island the boat was on the unsheltered sea, waves were rubbing and heaving their backs under it, this way and that way, turning it on the swell, letting it fall on its side, spilling them out, the sea running in, swallowing them.

Gulls shrieked overhead, but there was silence below the surface.

Chapter Seventeen

ANGE opened her eyes. There were boats around them, black on the water, arms reached out to them under a rattling square sail. Cold and warm came on her together, like frost and fire, as if she lay in a black keel burning on a bare hillside, dragons rising about her. Something all bone and feather whirled and haunted above her, dropping dismal thoughts and sorrows, a helicopter, a bird, a nightmare.

Dragon heads bowed and bobbed, about to peck; and foam fell like flame. She was pulled wet from the sea, and did not know what had rescued her.

Noise tore at her, not the steady crackle of falling leaves in frost, but the unsteady rush of a whole forest burning and heaving.

Overhead a black sail drummed; there was a tumult of tide and wind against the coast, the rocks combing them to fury, cliffs driving them sullen and dangerous on themselves.

Something hit Ange's head, a wet bundle. She opened her eyes. The bundle was Beowulf, looking out of his bag, his fur flat against him, his threadbare patches more prominent, his weight enormous with salt waters.

The boat was white, and blue, and there was red. It had no black sail. Ange was being carried on a sort of bed. Beyond a doorway there was warmth, without the bitter ends of heat and cold. Voices talked to one another, but none to her.

She woke up in a room with a green flashing ceiling, a blue flashing ceiling, a glowing red but still ceiling. She was taken out of the room like a loaf from an oven, slid out on to a wire rack, and raced away to cool. Beside her Beowulf was a loaf that had not risen, salt-damp, miserable.

Later Mum was with her, sitting in a strange chair and looking at Ange, not quite sure it was the right person.

'The others,' said Ange. Or perhaps Beowulf.

'Nothing to worry about,' said Mum, unhappily. 'Go to sleep.'

'Have we moved?' Ange asked. Her throat was full of sand. She could remember coughing rough water from her chest.

'Here tonight,' said Mum. 'Talk tomorrow.'

Tomorrow there was breakfast. Ange sat up in bed and found she was wearing a nightie never her own, and totally alien knickers. Beowulf was beside her, dry and fluffed out ridiculously, his eyes almost covered by fur.

Beyond a glass door Mum talked to a nurse. The nurse was Miss Norris, the eldest one. She was in charge, as she always was. Mum looked obedient. She came back to look at the breakfast, knowing how the rooms had to be run.

'You haven't finished,' she said, because Ange had only nibbled at each thing on the tray and hardly swallowed any; but the rules were to eat it all up. She had caught them from Miss Norris. There had been manna on the island, that angels eat. Ange had difficulties.

'It keeps swimming back up,' said Ange, miserably, knowing that worse was to come. Mum got the big bowl from the locker to her in time, and held her hair out of the way while whole waves of the sea foamed from her mouth.

Afterwards the room was dark with drawn curtains, needles of light throwing wands on the wall opposite. Outside there was traffic, and a scatter of bird song. Ange's bad moments had missed Beowulf. Mum picked him from the floor, waiting until

Ange spoke.

'Open the curtains,' said Ange, and blinked at the huge light pouring in from an overcast sky.

'How are you this time?' said Mum. 'Do you know?'

'Breakfast,' said Ange. She could smell food and liked it.

'Try some dinner,' said Mum. She went to get it, and watched Ange poke out the pieces she liked, then the pieces she did not like quite so much but had room for, and last the dull pieces, to round matters off.

Elfrida had thought it must be holy water, after the bitterness of the sea. It was scented and sweet and warm, and it went on and on, round and round, in the darkness.

'Something *is* happening,' she said. 'Beowulf, *where* are you?'

'Here,' said Beowulf, very relaxed after a good job done, and bathed in something like honey water.

'I am being washed *away*,' said Elfrida. 'Oh, I am coming *loose*. I am being *cleansed* out of my Bruin. I have *been* a hospitaller and infirmarian, and I know.'

'You'll be back,' said Beowulf. 'We've been through the washing machine before.'

'No,' said Elfrida, 'I am being *taken* away. I am going down the river to the *island*, with Cuddy. I am going to *Neorxenaw*—'

The word was bleached out of her. And after the first spin cycle she was no longer there. Beowulf called her name. There was no answer. Perhaps she too was now buried together in one place.

After hours of tumble-drying she was completely absent. But down past the cathedral, in the wrinkled river that received the hospital drain, there was a sailing away of fragrant song, fainter and fainter on the waters.

Ange got up for tea. Mum had brought a complete set of well-known clothes. Ange walked through into another room, rinsed clean of all she used to know, but reassembled. Mum closed the door after her and went away.

Ruth sat in a chair by the window, white and still. Robin was at a table with a magazine in front of him, but his eyes were not moving over its words. Edward sat alone, his eyes, nose, lips, red against a colourless face. Julian was looking out of the window but seeing nothing.

A man came in. 'Hello,' he said at once. 'My name's Roy. I've come to talk to you, and of course you know why.' He took a chair and sat at the table. 'I'll sit here, and you don't have to look at me. If you see me writing stuff down it's because we want to know what happened, not because we are going to turn your words on you. But, as you know, we have quite a serious problem, which we have to resolve to everybody's satisfaction. For the moment you need say nothing at all; in fact, if you want to walk out of the room you can. I'm not even going to ask for your names. When I've talked to you I'll write a report and let you see it, and until we agree that it's right no one else will read it. It's only an outline, and we can fill in details later.'

They were a long time about it. There were tangles to be unravelled, knots to undo, and plain pieces that would never lie down and be plain. From Ange's point of view there was no such thing as detail, because everything that had happened was an outline, and everything in the story was needed to complete it. And, by some instinct about this man Roy and what he wanted, no one mentioned the name or nature of Cuddy, only that he was a friend. This man, like Tyr, lived in one small room only, and had no landscapes to show.

'You were in Ancren Dale,' said Roy, firmly, when he felt he had a police sort of story. 'You were all together, and you were

185

joined by an old friend. I'll put in details of the friend, if that's what he was. But immediately you were in another place unknown to you, and walking towards the sea. The friend had some sort of fight, and then produced a boat from an unknown hiding place. You all got into the boat and went to an island. When you got there the friend left the boat, and the boat sank. You were picked up by some fishing boats, watched by a helicopter, transferred to a lifeboat, and brought ashore and into this hospital. I have more notes than that, and I'll put them into a longer narrative. If you like to tell me which one of you is which it will help to keep things straight for me. Someone will want to know some day, and you have said all the names. Ruth, that's you; Robin I had guessed; Julian is by the window; Ange is Anthea, the younger girl; and Edward is you? So the friend had a name and his name was Jude? How's that for an elementary deduction?' He smiled and gathered sheets of paper together. 'We'll want to know more about him, but now I think they're ready to take you home.'

'Jude?' said Ruth. 'I just thought she had gone home.'

'Jude is just a little girl,' said Robin. 'She was with us. What happened to her? She got out of the boat.'

'He told her not to,' said Ange. 'But she did.'

'It's like her,' said Edward. 'She always does what she wants. Jude Fitch.'

'No one mentioned her,' said Roy, his hand pausing on his papers, his face flushed red with dismay. 'None of your parents.'

'They didn't know,' said Ruth. 'But her mother would be looking for her. Wouldn't she?' She was not sure.

Roy understood. 'I'd better make enquiries,' he said. He went out of the room and began talking to mums and dads, and used a hospital telephone. Then he took his own portable from his pocket and went outside away from radio interference.

'He didn't ask,' said Ruth. 'I didn't know she wasn't here. She's drowned.'

'We can't tell him real things,' said Edward. 'He's like the rubbish salesmen who come to the pub and try to sell our Mum crap.'

Ange thought clearly of Jude alive, alive and tiresome, alive and picking a fight, alive and sulking, alive and charming things the way she wanted them, alive and saying things others would have said in some other way. Of Jude in the sea, silent, she could make no picture.

In twenty minutes Roy was back. 'No, well,' he said. 'I hope we understand some day, and it's natural you aren't clear about every detail even in the outline, but our local man has been down to see Mrs Fitch and Judith went off yesterday morning with her Dad to see her Granny, and she'll be back at six tonight. So I have to say there is a crack in your story, and we'll have to discuss it further, but not now. The hospital wants rid of you, so you're going home. Another day we'll sort out how you got thirty-five miles to the sea and a mile off shore in about an hour, with no means of transport. Meantime it's still abduction in our book, and when we ask again we'll have to know.'

He had come ready to believe anything, and left believing nothing, but unable to explain away what he could not understand. It was like that on the way home, and at home too. Something that had been mysterious enough to believe now had a false line that spoilt it all.

'But she was with us,' said Ange.

'Yes,' said Mum, very anxious about it all.

At some time after tea the telephone rang. Mum answered it carefully. Once it had been the police to say that Ange was half-drowned in the sea, quite beyond explanation. This time it was Edward's mother. Mum listened, said, 'Yes, yes,' bleakly, and came back into the room.

'Mrs Fitch has at last noticed that Jude did not go with her father the day before yesterday, has not been at her granny's, and is nowhere about. She casually mentioned it in the Swan Inn. So I am glad you are right, Anthea, but not glad about what you are right about.'

'I think this needs sorting out,' said Dad. 'You two can get on with it here, and I'll go down and talk to Mrs Obley, and anyone else. I know some strange things have happened round Jude, but they should not have ended like this. And it goes back a long way.'

He came home when Ange was asleep. Late at night she woke with the black boat heaving under her, and though she knew it was not moving, her mind swayed in her head, and the palpable waves of night broke against the house. Mum came and sat by her.

There was a truth to be got to, Dad said in the morning. 'As if it was written on a palimpsest, parchment that has been scraped clean and written over again. We must interpret it by looking at every detail. Often the truth isn't close by, but at the other side of fiction, and certainly stranger. Besides, I had similar thoughts in my head when I was young. They went away, but I spend my life dealing with such matters, and perhaps they caused that.'

Two afternoons later the three of them walked to Ancren Dale. 'We shall meet at the thorn tree,' said Dad. 'We must prove that the story hangs together. I believe Ange, and therefore the others. This is too odd not to be real.'

They were the first on the moor. At Ancren Dale other people began to appear. Down the side opposite came all three Miss Norrises, and their brother. At the top of the path from the village Edward and Robin were together. Ruth came through another way, driving a tractor, Julian with her to open the gates.

They went to the place where they had laid the relics, thinking they could see the box. But the box was a square block of sandstone, cut by nature, deep in a bed of grass and rushes. Beside it lay a plastic bag with an electric screwdriver in it.

'You put it on this?' Dad asked Ange.

'Just on the grass,' said Ange.

'This is the thing itself,' said Edward. 'The rock wasn't here, so the box must have fossilized since then. Jude put the marks on.'

'In five days?' said Dad, touching indentations. 'These are fossils, weather-worn. You might have thought they were pictures of some sort. But I've come here to find all the details, whatever their character.'

It is Jude's memorial, Ange thought. 'She drew them,' she said. 'In black paint.'

'It's not going to help Mrs Fitch,' said Mum. 'She has lost more than the truth.'

'And we have gained less,' said Dad. 'It isn't even a good story. We have to know the facts, and I accept what you say.'

'You will never believe it,' said Ruth. 'Or what we did.'

'You didn't believe me,' said Ange, 'when I heard a real bell. It was the otologist who knew that.'

'Me,' said Mr Norris. 'I said it was real, and it seems to have been.'

'What are we going to do?' said Dad. 'Something happened to Jude. We are guilty. I should have listened sooner.'

'I tried to write her out of the script,' said Robin, desolated. 'Did I do it?'

'She had the worst life,' said Edward. 'But she did most with it.'

189

There was a hollowness about standing in Ancren Dale together, gaining only regret, and sorrow for unknown things not done. Thoughts of Jude made Ange long for the moment to be over, but this solemn occasion could only end in its own time.

She was surprised to hear Edward and Robin arguing childishly. They should know better. But in turn they were surprised to hear other voices raised. Julian looked from one to another and listened elsewhere.

A child was shouting angrily. The voice was saying, 'I won't go, I won't. I am staying for ever.'

There had been a person with that ugly tone, though there no longer was. And at first there was nothing to see. Then, a little distance away there was an eddy in the air, a movement in which the air became visible, as if a flock of sheep might again appear. From that stir the voice came.

The movement grew clearer, and resolved into someone they knew. Jude stepped from another place into Ancren Dale, still expostulating and objecting. Some of the complaint was the calls of gulls in that other place.

'I *can* stay with you longer than a minute,' she said. 'I am not going away. Please, please, I want to stay for ever, you are my uncle, my grandfather, all my life. Only God loves you more than I do, and only God loves me more than you do. Please, *please*.'

The air closed behind her, and she was in the grasses of Ancren Dale with no one to plead with. Her arms clutched at air, but whatever place she had come from was closed to her.

She sat down, bowed her head, and wept loudly and truly, rubbing her face on her sleeve. Mum wanted to go to her, but did not, because the anguish in her weeping was so heartfelt that only its own ending would complete it. There was no comfort for Jude from outside; she had to be left to work out her sorrow.

The sorrow was coming no longer. Jude stood up, lifted her face up to the sky, and smiled with joy. 'Yes,' she said, 'yes, I shall, always.'

She seemed to watch something out of sight, or hear it out of hearing. When she had done so she turned to those in Ancren Dale and smiled on them.

'He wouldn't let me stay,' she said. 'So I've come back. He will look after me from Neorxenawang, but I shall always wish I could have stayed. You don't know about it, so I can't explain.'

'Your mother has been looking for you,' said Miss Norris. 'She thinks you have drowned.'

'She hasn't any water deep enough,' said Jude. 'I know that now. But I'd better go and see her. I wonder how old I have to be before leaving home.'

'You've been away long enough,' said Dad. 'We shall all see you home. We don't know what you will tell her, but we know where you came from.'

'But not where I'll go at last,' said Jude. She came to talk to Ruth, and walk with her, as an equal now, no longer a fretful child young for her years yet old in her wits. She was explaining her arguments with Cuddy, and admitting that he was right. 'I shan't quarrel any more,' she said. 'He doesn't, and that makes him right. I shall be useful here just never forgetting him. He's told me what to do, but I don't understand it all yet. It was a rough rackle-tackle journey back. Heck.'

At her house her mother came heavy to the door, indignant at being disturbed when she was mourning her only child. She was downright angry to have her flow interrupted by the child herself, tapping to be let in.

'What is it now?' she began. 'Is there no peace at all? Oh, it's you. Think how much this has cost me, and come inside. There's no tea for you, just your head in my hand.'

She gave Jude a smack behind the ear that almost made Ange fall over, right out of reach by the gate, but Jude was used to it. She took no notice. She turned to the others at the gate and smiled an encouraging smile.

Mrs Fitch glared at them. 'Hasn't she always been more trouble than she's worth!' she said. 'But I'll truly straighten her up now.' She banged the door, and could be heard bellowing in the room within.

'He should have kept her,' said Robin. 'She could have been happy.'

Over Ancren Dale a rainbow appeared, like Jude's smile.

'She will be happy,' said Ruth. 'She has changed. She is Cuddy's child now. We have all been his children.'

'Nice,' said Miss V Norris, without a word.

'Beowulf wants his tea,' said Ange. But Ruth had not meant that sort of childishness.

Beowulf was thinking, That's atelic; harder than ever I was hit, and I was eight times Jude's size. But now I am just a wrap-up of stuffing. And time has been slippery.

'He's only human,' said Ange. Dad held her hand.

Dad, having accepted facts, began to admit there was more than chance in it all. 'It's the way things kept turning up,' he said. 'Volumes of parchment with writing on, scraps of paper with other things on, flagstones talking nonsense in Anglo-Saxon. Some was Jude, but the rest I do not understand.'

Mum fussed over Beowulf, noticing he was wearing out. He squirmed, but could not get away.

'A biggish darning needle,' said Mum, with him firmly helpless. 'Such an awkward shape. And some stout thread.'

Ange went upstairs for thread. She had re-spun it and kept it

192

by. 'It's organic,' she said. 'Off a tree.'

'Well,' said Mum, wonderingly; and 'Well,' she said again, startled. 'He has little bones inside him.'

'He's a real bear,' said Ange. She remembered the poem: *Untamed he seeks for Honey wild, Or dances captive on the Street in Youth; Uncharming, fierce, far from Mild, His Gang cantankerous is called a Sleuth.*

'You know more about him than I do,' said Mum. 'There, that'll keep him together another thousand years.' It was only a guess.

One Saturday a week or two later Dad set up his study with a slide projector and an epidiascope to show pages against a screen. Jude came and watched politely, in her new way of being, silent when modern words were shown, MRS BEAR, and TOEFE.

'Mrs Beowulf,' she read. 'Toffee.'

Dad snorted at these moments of fancy, or not being able to read at her age. He began talking about damaged parchment, wondering why a monk needed to pierce the pages with regular lines of holes. He showed them on the screen, and Jude began to laugh.

'That's not damage,' she said scornfully. 'I wrote those words, and the holes are Granny's knitting pattern thing. She pokes the needle through to tell her what row she's at. She wants that back or I'll have grown out of the cardy before it's finished. She said. I knew I'd lost it somewhere.'

When Dad wanted to know how it had appeared on his desk at the University Library she remembered.

'It was daft for drawing on,' she said. 'I got a better bit of paper off your desk. I left that old rubbish from Keld House. I forgot about the knitting bit. I think I'll go home now so Granny can finish.'

She had her tea first, because that still seemed natural to her. She helped Beowulf to his, feeding him chocolate biscuits before leaving him in the coal scuttle.

'You've darned his bum,' she said, 'with a cross.'

'Part Christian,' said Dad. 'In a woolly way.'

'I'm Christian all over,' said Jude. 'Nearly.' She left with a polite thank you, and happily, taking the notebook once gathered up by Dad in one of his flurries and tipped out in the University Library.

'She's getting the manners of a saint,' said Mum.

'He's got a job on,' said Dad.

Ange, upstairs later on, had *An Infant's Bestiary* open and was reading another verse: *The Wolf with telling urgent Haste, Seeks to satisfy his Taste By eating Lambs or any Grandam, And Innocents he takes at Random.*

That's my address book, Beowulf thought. I wonder who I know? It's full of meat, I'm sure.

He had had no one to talk with for some time. Jude did not want him. Ange was not remembering him. I am alone, he thought. What did *she* say all the time? I wish it had been interesting. 'Elfrida? Bruin here. Bruin, you remember?'

There was no reply from Elfrida. But some other thing had been added and was stirring. Beowulf still had company.

Just a little itch where I have been darned. Why do I think of running in the dark, when sensible creatures sleep at night? Usually thrown out on the floor. But indoors every night, I'll say that for her. With Jude I'd be in the gutter. We'd be in the gutter.

He knew now what had been darned into him, and that the

sign of the cross made no difference: there were no Christians of that breed.

'Shut up, Beowulf,' said Ange.

But it was not Beowulf himself lifting a head and howling to the moon.

CUDDY was born thirteen and a half centuries ago, in 634. He was brought up by his aunt, Kenswith, sister to the king of Northumbria. When he was small he liked to show how athletic he was, beating all the other children at sports, until one of them told him to think of the real life ahead of him. Cuddy took that to heart, becoming a soldier for a time, then a shepherd. And he went on thinking. On the hillside one night he had a vision of angels taking the bright soul of a saint up to heaven and, learning that the great Aidan had just died, he knew he must leave his sheep and join a monastery.

He became a missionary in the hills of Northumbria. His life was filled with strange events and miracles, even on days off as a tourist among Roman remains in Carlisle. He became Prior of Lindisfarne, but preferred to live out at sea alone on the island of Inner Farne, talking to otters. He was obliged, though, to return to Lindisfarne to be its Bishop. When he felt his life was ending he went back to the island, to die there on 20th March 687, aged fifty-four. His last meal was of home-grown onions, St Bede tells us.

Cuddy wanted to be buried on the island, but his monks could not bear to leave him, and took him back to Lindisfarne. Eleven years later they found him still flexible and sweet, as if he slept peacefully. This showed them that he was an uncorrupted saint.

Viking raiders, coming to Lindisfarne by night eighty years later, did not care. They ignored Cuddy, but stole his treasure and killed monks. The Saint's People, a special brotherhood of monks, took him out of danger, carrying the Corsaint, containing him and certain articles of his, to safe places over the next one hundred and twenty years. When the country was peaceful again, a thousand years ago now, his final resting-place was Durham. The Cathedral dedicated to him was built round his shrine, and many other churches were later named after him. He was last touched in 1547 by the man officially destroying the shrine with 'the great fore-hammer of a smith', who found him still fresh and sweet – although his coffin was nested in by a weasel in the time of St William of Carileph.

Recently it was clear to me that part of Cuddy, between body and soul, had to return to his island, but only when the descendants of the Saint's People were ready to see to it and able to do so. As for Beowulf and Elfrida, well, that was one of many miracles. Perhaps Jude is to be another.

WM

The Candle Man
Catherine Fisher

An eerie tale of the supernatural...

*M*eurig the fiddler is a haunted man. The evil water spirit, Hafren, has captured his soul – and now possesses the key... to his life.

The Severn was grey and purple; huge, a shifting, breathing mass of water, swollen right up to the base of the wall, lapping quietly.

About half a mile down the wall was the watchtower, tall and built of black stone, its windows blank eyes that watched them come.

Conor hesitated. Then he said, 'Do you think it will be... safe?'

Meurig turned. 'Safe?'

'Yes. You know.'

The fiddler glanced out at the estuary. 'You mean from the water?'

'Yes.'

They looked at each other for a moment. Then the fiddler smiled a bitter smile. 'I doubt it. For me, nowhere is safe.'

THE CANDLE MAN by Catherine Fisher
RED FOX paperback, £2.99 ISBN 0 09 930139 3

THE Forestwife

*I*t's the reign of Richard the Lionheart, a time
when girls obey their elders without question.
But not Mary – she's got plans. Why marry an old
widower when she can live in the forest learning the
ancient arts of herbalism, green magic and healing?
And, who knows? She might also find true friendship
and even... love.

Here's a spellbinding snippet...

Mary and Agnes turned to see a young boy carrying a
smaller child. He stood in the clearing in front of the
cottage, looking fearfully from the stone pointer towards
the doorway.
'Can I help thee, lad?' said Agnes.
'Art thou the Forestwife?'
Though the lad spoke up firmly, his face was white and
his bare knees shook.
Agnes looked down at Selina's girdle. The intricately
woven belt lay across the palms of her hands. She hesitated
for a moment, but then she dropped the rug and cloak.
Her face was solemn and pale as she fastened the girdle
around her waist.
'Aye,' she said. 'I am the Forestwife.'

RED FOX paperback, £2.99, ISBN 0 09 926431 5

THE *Herring Girls*

*T*heresa Tomlinson blends fact with fiction in
her moving account of thirteen-year-old Dory,
caught up in the close-knit, hard-working fishing
community of Whitby. Dory's determined to be a
strong, fast worker – but has she got what it takes
to be a real herring girl?

Here's a preview to get you hooked...

I took the sharpest knife from my pocket and picked up a
good-sized fish, trying hard to remember what Hannah
had taught me. I pushed the knife in carefully and twisted
it, and the guts flew out into the gut tub.

The man grunted. 'Now size?' he snapped.

'Mattiefull,' I answered him, my voice all shaky.

'What?' He put his hand to his ear.

'Mattiefull,' I said loudly.

He nodded and pointed to the basket behind me.
slipped the fish in and snatched up another herring to gu

Nelly pushed in beside me and set to work. Mary Jan
went to pack the barrel behind us.

I paused to watch Nelly for a moment and my mouth
dropped open. Nelly could certainly gip, and she could gi
fast. She'd done four fish while I did one.

'Stop gawping,' she muttered under her breath. 'Ge
gipping!'

RED FOX paperback, £3.50, ISBN 0 09 936311 9

Dancing
THROUGH THE
Shadows

THERESA TOMLINSON

'What's the most precious thing on earth?
Not money, not gold or silver...'

Sometimes you don't know what the most important
things in life are - until you've lost them. But now and
then you're given the chance to you understand, with
one crystal clear thought, how much something - or
someone - really means. That's what Ellen discovers
when her safe, secure world is rocked by the news that
her mum has breast cancer. And suddenly Ellen
realises that the best things in her life have been right
in front of her eyes all the time - she was just too blind
to see them.

Dancing Through the Shadows by Theresa Tomlinson
Red Fox paperback, £3.99 ISBN 0 09 920792 3

The Trokeville Way

RUSSELL HOBAN

**Shortlisted for the Guardian Children's Fiction Prize
and the Whitbread Children's Book of the Year 1996**

Turbocharged. That's how Nick Hartley's head feels.
Everything's too bright; everyone's too intense. And just
when he thinks life can't get any more bizarre, fate leads
Nick to the Juzzle. Part picture, part puzzle, the Juzzle
becomes Nick's ticket to the mind trip of a lifetime; a
doorway through to an action-packed alternative reality,
a weird parallel world and a very different,
very scary, very strange state of mind...

'Quirky, marvellously original... unpredictable and unexpected'
DAILY TELEGRAPH

THE TROKEVILLE WAY by Russell Hoban
Red Fox paperback, £3.50 ISBN 0 09 967981 7